INSIDE STORIES

2

Peter and Susan Benton

Hodder & Stoughton

A MEMBER OF THE HODDER HEADLINE GROUP

British Library Cataloguing in Publication Data

Benton, Peter
  Inside Stories. – Book 2
  I. Title II. Benton, Susan
  823.0108

  ISBN 0-340-50359-9

First published 1993
Impression number 10 9 8 7 6 5 4 3 2
Year   1998 1997 1996 1995 1994

Typeset by Keyset Composition, Colchester, Essex.
Printed in Great Britain for Hodder & Stoughton Educational, a division
of Hodder Headline Plc, 338 Euston Road, London NW1 3BH
by The Bath Press, Avon.

♣

CONTENTS

TO THE TEACHER

There are stories in every culture and, as far as we know, stories have existed in all past ages. A French or a Chinese child of the twelfth or the nineteenth century would have heard stories just as surely as the child in medieval England or the Victorian nursery. A child in ninth century China may have heard what is essentially the story of Cinderella a thousand years before his or her counterpart in Europe was delighted by the Perrault version. Aesop's fables of two thousand five hundred years ago were not even then altogether new and had their counterparts in tales from Egypt, Babylon, India and elsewhere. Many of the parables and allegorical stories of the Bible have their parallels in other faiths.

Today's children may hear stories read at bedtime, at school, in their place of worship, on tape, on radio and on television. They will tell each other stories both real and imagined: as small children they may make up stories, imaginary friends, fantasies that may delight or frighten. Later, they may become voracious readers, devouring stories from the printed pages of books and magazines. Some may enjoy writing their own stories from a very early age. In a sense, the play of making up stories is the work of the child, for through story we make sense of the world. We have an insatiable appetite for stories, whether as children or as adults: even those who are not great readers of books may well be passionately committed to following the twists and turns of the soap opera on television, the daily unfolding of a seemingly endless story – which may possibly extend over twenty years or more. All the time we are absorbing the structures and patterns of stories, and many people who would never be great *writers* of stories have a skill as story*tellers* that makes them popular wherever they go. For the world loves a good story.

It seems that human beings *need* stories and, whatever our age or whatever our role, we are the main characters in the story we weave about ourselves. Stories are a way in which we represent the world to ourselves and, in the stories we tell ourselves or others, stories also become a way in which we represent ourselves to the world. They also help us to understand experiences we may never have had personally – of another time, another place, another culture. Stories allow us to speculate about 'what if. . .?' Stories are the foundations of religions and of history. The culture and the beliefs of a society are deeply embedded in its stories. For both individuals and societies live by the stories they tell themselves.

Stories delight, entertain, relax and instruct, but they are not value-free. It is important to be able not only to enjoy the stories we read but to see where they are coming from and where they would lead us. To do this we need to have some understanding of how stories work, how their effects are achieved.

Inside Stories 2, the second book in this four-volume series, is concerned to assist students explore the nature and roots of story, the act of reading and their own critical response, rather than to offer merely 'comprehension-type' activities. It is geared to the needs of pupils working towards Key Stage 3 and it reflects, we believe, the needs of teachers of such groups. The range of authors represents some of the best of modern story writers of several nationalities, reflecting the view that the range of stories presented in classrooms should be diverse and multicultural. In addition, we have throughout the series attempted to promote an awareness of the roots of story such as those in fairy story, classical myth and legend, and the Bible. This volume also includes traditional fables, etiological tales and tall stories which have their roots in the oral tradition.

In common with the other books of this series, *Inside Stories 2* is divided into two main sections. In each volume, *Section A – Exploring Stories* is a 'teaching section' which focuses on specific aspects of storytelling or on types of story. *Section B* is a teaching anthology of stories loosely linked by theme into sections – in this volume, *Tricksters and Riddlers*, *Strange to Tell* and *From Four to Fourteen*. While acknowledging that any such sectionalisation is far from perfect, it does, we believe, help the teacher to present disparate material in a manageable fashion. Teachers should not feel bound by the sections, however, and should cut across these artificial boundaries – or introduce other material from outside – whenever it seems appropriate.

Each story is accompanied by a teaching section – *Inside the Story*. The aim of this section is to prompt students to think more deeply about what they have read, about how it operates and about how they respond. In almost every case we have suggested pair or group discussion as a way into the text in the firm belief that one has to start with the student's own perceptions about the story before one can proceed further, and that the sharing of such perceptions is, in itself, a valuable activity. Nonetheless, we recognise that there may be occasions when the teacher judges that a preliminary written response may be more appropriate for a particular group. There are, of course, suggestions for students' own writing as well as for oral work at the end of each story.

The activities related to the text are wide ranging and are designed to further understanding of the structures and techniques used by tellers and writers of stories. They offer opportunities for creative and critical responses, for discussion, writing, interviewing, tape-recording and performance. These tasks cover the range of activities which are seen as being appropriate at all levels for the

National Curriculum in English. We share the belief that pupils should be encouraged towards an active engagement with stories which stresses reading and response rather than comprehension and criticism. Small group work and shared experiences of stories are valuable, and wide ranging writing tasks as well as the more common writing of stories and reviews are encouraged. We believe that pupils should increasingly be made aware of the elements of story structure and encouraged to use more consciously crafted techniques in their own writing of stories and we have designed the talking and writing assignments with this end in view. The stories and tasks proposed vary greatly in difficulty and complexity; thus the book aims to cater for a very wide range of readers and it will be possible for individuals to follow their own interests at their own level – perhaps branching out beyond the immediate context of this collection where they find an area that they wish to explore further.

We have suggested ways into the material, but the teacher is the best judge of what is appropriate for which students and will modify the approaches in the light of his or her close knowledge of the class. This is not a course to be followed slavishly and, for all its serious purpose, we hope it is a book to be enjoyed.

Peter and Susan Benton, Oxford 1993

♣

ACKNOWLEDGEMENTS

The publishers would like to thank the following for their kind permission to reproduce material in this volume:

Oxford University Press for 'Thunder and Lightning' from *African Myths and Legends* retold by Kathleen Arnott (O.U.P. 1962) and 'The Price of Greed' from *Indian Tales and Legends* retold by J. E. B. Gray (O.U.P. 1961); Faber and Faber Ltd for 'Lutey and the Mermaid' from *The Carpenter and other stories* by Susan Price (Faber and Faber, 1981); Beverley Hoult for 'Why the Bear has a Stumpy Tail' by Kathleen Lines from The Faber Story Book ed. Kathleen Lines (Faber and Faber, 1961); J. M. Dent & Sons Ltd for 'The Wedding at Stanton Drew' and 'The Ghost of Lady Hobby' both from *Everyman's Book of English Folk Tales* (J. M. Dent & Sons, 1981); Andre Deutsch Ltd for 'Tall Story' by Jean Anselme (translated by Michael Benedikt) from *Ring Around the World* (Rapp & Whiting Ltd); Poolbeg Press Limited for 'The House Under the Sea' from *The Bridge of Feathers* by Eamon Kelly (Poolbeg Press, 1989); Penguin Books Ltd for 'William's Version' by Jan Mark from *Nothing to be Afraid of* © Jan Mark (Viking Kestrel, 1977 and Puffin Books, 1980) and for 'The Rainbow Clock' by Susan Gregory from *Martini on the rocks* © Susan Gregory (Viking Kestrel, 1984 and in Puffin Books); David Higham Associates for 'John Pettigrew's Mirror' by Ruth Manning-Sanders from *Ghost Stories* ed. Robert Westall (Kingfisher Books, 1988); Longman Group UK Limited for 'Tiger and Anancy Meet Fi War' by James Berry from *The Girls and Yanga Marshall* by James Berry (Longman, 1987); Pavilion Books Ltd for 'Two Giants' by Edna O'Brien from *Tales For the Telling: Irish Folk and Fairy Stories* (Pavilion Books); D. M. Thomas for 'What Happens at School' by Sean Thomas from *Allsorts 3* ed. Ann Thwaite (Macmillan, 1970 and Pan Books, 1973).

The publishers would like to thank the following for giving permission to reproduce the following copyright illustrations:

p7, from *African Myths and Legends*, retold by Kathleen Arnott (1962) © Oxford University Press 1962. Reproduced by permission of Oxford University Press; p8, from *The Faber Storybook*, edited by Kathleen Lines and illustrated by Alan Howard. Reproduced by permission of Faber and Faber Ltd; p16, 19, by John Lawrence; p22, © PEANUTS characters 1952, 1960 UFS, Inc. Reprinted by permission; p28, 29, Mary Evans Picture Library; p38, 39, Editions Denoel Sarl; p40, 42, ANANCY SPIDERMAN. Illustrations © 1988 by Joseph Olubo. Published in the UK by Walker Books Limited; p44, from *Indian Tales and Legends* retold by J. E. B Gray (1961) © Oxford University Press 1961. Reproduced by permission of Oxford University Press; p49, 52, 74, 76, by Jacqui Thomas in *Stories Around The World*, published by Hodder and Stoughton Publishers; p56, 82, by Corinna Sargood, from *The Virago Book of Fairy Tales*. Reproduced by arrangement with Rogers, Coleridge and White Ltd, London; p68, from *Ghost Stories*, edited by Robert Westall and illustrated by Sean Eckett. Published by Kingfisher Books © Grisewood & Dempsey 1993.

Every effort has been made to trace and acknowledge ownership of copyright. The publishers will be glad to make suitable arrangements with any copyright holders it has not been possible to contact.

SECTION A:
EXPLORING STORIES

1
ORIGINS AND EXPLANATIONS

People have always made up stories to explain things which seem strange or outside their control. These stories are known as myths. They often involve supernatural beings such as gods, giants and monsters, or humans with magical powers, since no ordinary mortal could possibly influence events such as earthquakes, storms or volcanic eruptions.

We still make up stories today to explain things we don't understand. Recently there has been much talk about crop circles appearing in fields of wheat. Some claim they are all a hoax and that the circles are made by jokers using planks of wood; some claim that the explanation is scientific and that the circles are the result of electrical charges in the atmosphere. But many people claim that the circles are the result of alien visitors from outer space landing their craft in lonely spots. If you don't understand it, a good story will always help to fill the gap.

The Netsilik Inuit people were puzzled to find fossils of sea creatures and plants on hilltops far from the sea. So, they invented a tale of how in the days before humans existed, a giant fell into the sea. As he did so, water was carried far into the land, taking with it animals and plants. When the waters eventually receded, these animals and plants were left stranded on the dry land. They dried out into the fossils, shells, bones and plants which we see today.

From southern Italy comes the story of a little girl who discovered a dragon living beneath the nearby mountain. The fire and smoke he breathed and the heaving of the earth as he moved were responsible for the eruptions of the volcano.

Every culture has its own myth to explain the daily rising and setting of the sun. The ancient Greeks believed it was the god Helios who drove across the sky each day in his chariot, from his palace in the east to his palace in the west. During the night he was carried in a boat along the Ocean stream which flows round the world, back to his palace in the east. The ancient Egyptians explained it as the god Horus sailing each day across the sky in his golden boat of the sun. Each night the boat had to sail through the Duat, or land of the dead, and in the last region of the night the god had to fight the dragon Apophis and defeat him before the sun could rise again.

In ancient China a tale was told of a boy who behaved courteously to a strange traveller and his four servants, offering them food and shelter. The stranger turned out to be the yellow dragon who controlled the storms and his servants the four winds. Of course, the boy was rewarded for his hospitality; his home was spared when the tempest devastated the surrounding countryside.

People have always been frightened by storms and the damage they can do. It is not surprising that there are many stories to explain what they are and where they come from. The following explanation comes from Nigeria.

THUNDER AND LIGHTNING

Kathleen Arnott

A long time ago, both thunder and lightning lived on this earth, among all the people. Thunder was an old mother sheep and Lightning was her son, a handsome ram, but neither animal was very popular.

When anybody offended the ram, Lightning, he would fly into a furious rage and begin burning down huts and corn bins, and even knock down large trees. Sometimes he damaged crops on the farms with his fire and occasionally he killed people who got in his way.

As soon as his mother, Thunder, knew he was behaving in this evil way, she would raise her voice and shout as loudly as she could, and that was very loud indeed.

Naturally the neighbours were very upset, first at the damage caused by Lightning and then by the unbearable noise that always followed his outbursts. The villagers complained to the king on many occasions, until at last he sent the two of them to live at the very edge of the village, and said that they must not come and mix with people any more.

However, this did no good, since Lightning could still see people as they walked about the village streets and so found it only too easy to continue picking quarrels with them. At last the king sent for them again.

'I have given you many chances to live a better life,' he said, 'but I can see that it is useless. From now on, you must go right away from our village and live in the wild bush. We do not want to see your faces here again.'

Thunder and Lightning had to obey the king and left the village, angrily cursing its inhabitants.

Alas, there was still plenty of trouble in store for the villagers, since Lightning was so angry at being banished that he now set fire to the whole bush, and during the dry season this was extremely unfortunate. The flames spread to the little farms which the people had planted, and sometimes to their houses as well, so that they were in despair again. They often heard the mother ram's mighty voice calling her son to order, but it made very little difference to his evil actions.

The king called all his councillors together and asked them to advise him, and at last they hit on a plan. One white-headed elder said:

'Why don't we banish Thunder and Lightning right away from the earth? Wherever they live there will be trouble, but if we sent them up into the sky, we should be rid of them.'

So Thunder and Lightning were sent away into the sky, where the people hoped they would not be able to do any more damage.

Things did not work out quite as well as they had hoped, however, for Lightning still loses his temper from time to time and cannot resist sending fire down to the earth when he is angry. Then you can hear his mother rebuking him in her loud rumbling voice.

Occasionally even his mother cannot bear to stay with him and goes away for a little while. You will know when this happens, for Lightning still flashes his fire on the earth, but his mother is so far away that she does not see, and her voice is silent.

Inside the story

In pairs

1 Why do you think a sheep and a ram were chosen to represent Thunder and Lightning in this story? Would, say, a tortoise and a pig have been equally suitable?

2 Look again at the last paragraph and think about what it is explaining.

On your own

Think of other animals which would make suitable characters in a story about thunder and lightning, either because of their behaviour or the way they move. Write and illustrate your own thunder and lightning myth using animals of your choice.

Many of the early myths attempted to explain why different animals behaved or looked as they did. This particular one comes from Norway, but some people know it better as a North American tale about Brer Fox.

WHY THE BEAR HAS A STUMPY TAIL

Kathleen Lines

One day in mid-winter, the Fox came slinking home with a string of fish he had stolen, when he met the Bear.

'Where did you get those fish?' asked the Bear.

'Oh, my lord Bruin, I've been out fishing and caught them,' said the Fox.

So the Bear had a mind to learn to fish too, and bade the Fox tell him how to set about it.

'Oh, it is an easy craft,' answered the Fox, 'and soon learned. You've only to go out upon the ice and cut a hole and stick your tail down into it; and so you must stay, holding it there as long as you can. You must not mind if your tail smarts a little – that is when the fish bite. The longer you hold it there, the more fish you will get; and then, all at once, out with it, with a cross pull sideways, and a strong pull too.'

Well, the Bear did as the Fox said, and held his tail a long, long time down in the hole, till it was fast frozen in. Then he pulled it out, with a cross pull sideways, and it snapped right off. And that is why the bear goes about with only a stump of a tail to this very day.

Stories that explain the way animals look and behave have caught the imagination of more modern writers too. Rudyard Kipling's *Just So Stories* and Ted Hughes's *How the Whale Became* both take the question of how different animals came to be the way they are and suggest some ingenious, and amusing, explanations. Here is Kipling's explanation of how the camel got his hump. Rudyard Kipling liked to illustrate his own stories and usually made the first letter of each of his *Just So Stories* into a picture. Can you see the N of 'Now' in the shape of the Camel?

HOW THE CAMEL GOT HIS HUMP
Rudyard Kipling

ow this is the next tale, and it tells how the Camel got his big hump.

In the beginning of years, when the world was so new-and-all, and the Animals were just beginning to work for Man, there was a Camel, and he lived in the middle of a Howling Desert because he did not want to work; and besides, he was a Howler himself. So he ate sticks and thorns and tamarisks and milkweed and prickles, most 'scruciating idle; and when anybody spoke to him he said 'Humph!' Just 'Humph!' and no more.

Presently the Horse came to him on Monday morning, with a saddle on his back and a bit in his mouth, and said, 'Camel, O Camel, come out and trot like the rest of us.'

'Humph!' said the Camel; and the Horse went away and told the Man.

Presently the Dog came to him, with a stick in his mouth, and said, 'Camel, O Camel, come and fetch and carry like the rest of us.'

'Humph!' said the Camel; and the Dog went away and told the Man.

Presently the Ox came to him, with the yoke on his neck, and said, 'Camel, O Camel, come and plough like the rest of us.'

'Humph!' said the Camel; and the Ox went away and told the Man.

At the end of the day the Man called the Horse and the Dog and the Ox together, and said, 'Three, O Three, I'm very sorry for you (with the world so new-and-all); but that Humph-thing in the Desert can't work, or he would have been here by now, so I am going to leave him alone, and you must work double-time to make up for it.'

That made the Three very angry (with the world so new-and-all), and they held a palaver, and an *indaba*, and a *punchayet*, and a pow-wow on the edge of the Desert; and the Camel came chewing milkweed *most* 'scruciating idle, and laughed at them. Then he said 'Humph!' and went away again.

Presently there came along the Djinn in charge of All Deserts, rolling in a cloud of dust (Djinns always travel that way because it is Magic), and he stopped to palaver and pow-wow with the Three.

'Djinn of All Deserts,' said the Horse, '*is* it right for any one to be idle, with the world so new-and-all?'

'Certainly not,' said the Djinn.

'Well,' said the Horse, 'there's a thing in the middle of your Howling Desert (and he's a Howler himself) with a long neck and long legs, and he hasn't done a stroke of work since Monday morning. He won't trot.'

'Whew!' said the Djinn, whistling, 'that's my Camel, for all the gold in Arabia! What does he say about it?'

'He says "Humph!"' said the Dog; 'and he won't fetch and carry.'

'Does he say anything else?'

'Only "Humph!"; and he won't plough,' said the Ox.

'Very good,' said the Djinn. 'I'll humph him if you will kindly wait a minute.'

The Djinn rolled himself up in his dust-cloak, and took a bearing across the desert, and found the Camel most 'scruciatingly idle, looking at his own reflection in a pool of water.

'My long and bubbling friend,' said the Djinn, 'what's this I hear of your doing no work, with the world so new-and-all?'

'Humph!' said the Camel.

The Djinn sat down, with his chin in his hand, and began to think a Great Magic, while the Camel looked at his own reflection in the pool of water.

'You've given the Three extra work ever since Monday morning, all on account of your 'scruciating idleness,' said the Djinn; and he went on thinking Magics, with his chin in his hand.

'Humph!' said the Camel.

'I shouldn't say that again if I were you,' said the Djinn; 'you might say it once too often. Bubbles, I want you to work.'

And the Camel said 'Humph!' again; but no sooner had he said it than he saw his back, that he was so proud of, puffing up and puffing up into a great big lolloping humph.

'Do you see that?' said the Djinn. 'That's your very own humph that you've brought upon your very own self by not working. To-day is Thursday, and you've done no work since Monday, when the work began. Now you are going to work.'

'How can I,' said the Camel, 'with this humph on my back?'

'That's made a-purpose,' said the Djinn, 'all because you missed those three days. You will be able to work now for three days without eating, because you can live on your humph; and don't you ever say I never did anything for you. Come out of the Desert and go to the Three, and behave. Humph yourself!'

And the Camel humphed himself, humph and all, and went away to join the Three. And from that day to this the Camel always wears a humph (we call it 'hump' now, not to hurt his feelings); but he has never yet caught up with the three days that he missed at the beginning of the world, and he has never yet learned how to behave.

Inside the story

In small groups

1 Rudyard Kipling's story of the camel's hump is best if you read it aloud. In your group prepare a reading of the story. You will need a voice for each of the characters – Horse, Camel, Dog, Ox, Man, Djinn – and a Storyteller to read the linking parts; you might also like to add sound effects to represent the howling desert and to suggest the Djinn's magic working. When you have practised your reading, record it onto tape or perform it to the rest of the class.

2 If you have a copy of Rudyard Kipling's *Just So Stories* or of Ted Hughes's *How the Whale Became* in your school library, look up some of their other explanations of animal origins. Different groups in the class could then choose to perform different stories and you could produce a class tape of your favourites. Or you could simply retell the stories to the class in your own words.

On your own

1 Jot down a list of animals as they come to mind; when you have thought of several, alongside each one write what its particular features or characteristics are:

Giraffe	long neck and legs, special skin pattern.
Elephant	size, wrinkled tough skin, trunk instead of a nose, ivory tusks, very small tail, large flapping ears.
Rhinoceros	bulky; tough armoured skin, tiny eyes, horn.
Duck-billed platypus	. . . . . .lots of possibilities here!

2 Choose one of the animals you have listed and write your own myth explaining why it is as it is; don't forget to include behaviour as well as appearance. You might find it helps to start by asking yourself, 'What does it look *like*? What might people have thought happened to the creature to make it go like that? *Why* might it have happened?'

You may also find it helps to write the story as though for younger children, maybe for a class in the local junior school.

The finished stories can be word-processed and illustrated; you can then put them together into a class booklet or a wall display. Best of all, you might arrange to take your stories into a junior school class and read them to the children.

2
THE SPIRIT OF THE PLACE

Groups of people who have settled in the same place and have a history of living together as a community gradually develop their own local stories. These may be about people who lived there in the past, for example highwaymen, murderers, witches, wise women, fools and tricksters; or they may be about ghosts and strange happenings, or about the stupidity of the inhabitants of neighbouring towns or villages.

Some stories linked to particular places may date back centuries to pagan times when people believed that every spring of fresh water, every grove of trees, every mountain had its own spirit – what the Romans called a 'genius loci' or Spirit of the Place. Even today, many people believe that places such as Stonehenge and Glastonbury are magical sites of ancient power.

There are also plenty of stories of this kind about natural features, for, in imagination, strangely shaped rocks and hills are easily transformed into kingly graves, sleeping dragons or whatever takes people's fancy. How many Devil's Leaps there must be across the world – chasms no human being could jump!

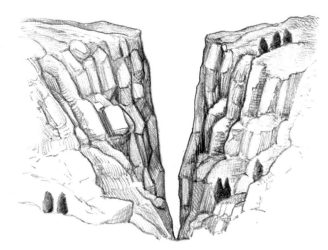

Massive stone structures like the pyramids of Egypt, the Inca temples of South America or the stone circles of Britain have always fascinated people. They simply cry out to be explained by stories, for people find it hard to believe that such huge structures could have been erected by ordinary humans in the past. So, they say, it must have been magic, giants or even creatures from outer space who put up Stonehenge.

In Oxfordshire, the Rollright Stones form a stone circle, with a group of larger stones standing together close by. The local story is that the stones are the petrified bodies of a king and his knights who were tricked by a witch. She turned them all to stone with the words:

Thou and thy men hoar stones shall be
And I myself an elder tree.

Local legend has it that, when the clock strikes midnight, the King stone and his stone men go down to the river to drink. In the last century local people believed that elder trees in the area would bleed if a blade was stuck into their bark. If an elder tree was cut at midnight on Midsummer Eve, it was believed that the tree would bleed and the King stone would turn his head.

Such stories were passed on by word of mouth from person to person and from generation to generation in what is known as an 'oral tradition'. However strange the tale, it needed to be at least partly believed by the teller and there had to be enough truth in it to enable listeners to believe it if it was going to survive.

The following story accounts for the existence of another stone circle, this time at Stanton Drew in Somerset.

THE WEDDING AT STANTON DREW

Sybil Marshall

At the sweet time of the year when spring slips unnoticed into summer, when the swallows are back and buttercups yellow the fields, when evening dusk merges into mellow moonlight, and the night is almost as warm as the day, it is the right time for weddings – especially in a village where everything keeps tune with the rhythm of the seasons. So it was at Stanton Drew, a tiny village on the banks of the River Chew in Somerset, many, many, many years ago. The day was a balmy Saturday, when the bride and the groom and all their family and friends walked to the church for the marriage ceremony and the blessing of the priest upon the young couple's union. That over, they set about the business of enjoying themselves, and making the most of the chance of jollity, with eating and drinking, and the romping merriment of rustic music and dance.

When early evening came, the local harpist came too; and out into a field close by the church the wedding party went, to form up their sets and take their places for the age old country dances in which grace and elegance give way to strength and agility, and the figures only stop when dancers and musicians alike run out of breath.

As dance succeeded dance, the party grew merrier and merrier, and the feet of the company more nimble. None was more nimble than the bride, whose sparkling eyes and rosy cheeks grew ever more excited and whose laughter rang ever more loud and abandoned.

The moon was high, the night was calm, and time slipped by as if on magic wings. They were in the very middle of a dance when the harpist suddenly drew his fingers across the strings with a firm chord, and the music drifted into silence. The dancers stood waiting for him to continue, but they could see that he was making preparations to pack up.

The bride left her place in the figure and ran across to him. 'What's the matter?' she asked. 'Why are you stopping?'

He pointed up to the moon. 'It is time to stop,' he said. 'It is now midnight, and in a few minutes it will be the Sabbath Day.'

'What does that matter?' said the excited girl. 'I shall only be married once, and I shall dance all night if I want to!'

The pious old musician was shocked. 'Then you will have to find somebody else to play for you,' he answered, 'for I will not profane the sabbath.' And he continued to pack up his harp.

Then the bride pleaded, and coaxed, and cajoled to prevail on him to stay; but he shook his head, and prepared to leave. At this the girl flew into a passion, and turned her pleadings to abuse. 'Go then, you miserable old spoilsport,' she yelled. 'We'll dance without you and your music! I'll find somebody else to play for one more dance, if I have to go to Hell to get him!'

As the old man shuffled off towards home in the moonlight, the angry shouts of the disappointed revellers followed him into the night; and as they turned dejectedly to follow him, since they could not dance without music, they saw approaching from the opposite way the outline of a stranger. He came upon them out of the night, and they saw that he was old, but most impressive looking, with exceedingly bright eyes and a long venerable beard.

'Give you greetings!' he said pleasantly. 'I heard the sounds of a quarrel as I came towards you. Now what can be wrong with a merry party on such a beautiful night?'

Then the bride, in tears of anger, told the courteous old stranger how the harpist with his religious scruples had taken himself off at midnight, and put an end to all their fun.

'If that's all, it can soon be mended,' said the old man. 'I will play for you myself.' And he sat down on a convenient boulder, took a pipe from under his cloak, and began to play.

It seemed at first that his fingers were stiff and out of practice, but he soon caught up the rhythm again, and choosing their partners for a round dance, they began to move to his music. After a minute or two, he began to quicken his tempo, and the dancers felt their feet responding to the urgent music in a way they had never done before with their familiar harpist. Faster and faster the new musician played, and faster and faster they whirled in breathless, mad abandon, till the peace of the holy sabbath was shattered with their wild laughter and cries of merriment. On and on went the music, and on and on went the dance, until all were breathless and exhausted, and longing to sit down and rest.

'Stop!' cried the bride, gasping for air. 'Stop and let us rest.' But the piper took no notice, so they decided to stop of their own accord and fling themselves down on the grass to recover. It was then they found out that they had no control over their feet at all, and that while the music went on, they had no option but to go on dancing to it. Seeing their predicament, the piper lifted his head, and played louder, and stronger, and faster, faster, ever faster, till the gasps of the dancers turned to moans, and their merry cries to groans, and their laughter to wails as their pleas for mercy died away for lack of breath with which to utter them. And still the relentless music went on, and still their feet rose and fell in time with it, hour after hour as the night wore on, and the moon sank, leaving them still dancing in the darkness.

At last the first streaks of dawn began to show in the eastern sky, and faint hope began to rise in their hearts that with the new day their terrible ordeal must end. So it proved, for as the first rays of the morning sun struck him, their strange musician put down his pipe and stood up. The circle of exhausted dancers immediately stopped in their tracks, and stood as if frozen solid with horror! For protruding from beneath his robe was an unmistakable cloven hoof, from under his hood they spied a pair of unmistakable horns, and behind him they saw the end of an unmistakable forked tail. While they stood as if petrified with terror, still in the strange attitudes of their exhaustion, he put away his pipe, and turned towards them.

'I'll come back, and play for you again, one day,' he chuckled, and walked away into the morning. And as they watched the Devil depart, for it was surely none other than he, so they became petrified in truth, and turned to pillars of stone where they stood.

There they stand to this very day, the inner circle of three sets of standing stones, in a field close by the church at Stanton Drew; and there they will stay, it is supposed, until the Fiend returns to play for them again, as he promised to do all those many centuries ago, when knowingly they chose to break the sabbath for the sake of one more dance.

It is not surprising that there are many stories linked with the sites of ancient battles. Often they tell of ghostly soldiers re-appearing on the anniversary of the battle, or being seen at midnight.

The most famous of these tales is probably that of 'The Battle of Edge Hill'. On Sunday, 23 October 1642, the Royalist army of King Charles I met the Parliamentary army of Oliver Cromwell. Forty thousand men took part in the bitter and bloody fighting; by the end of the day the field was littered with the bodies of the dead and wounded, and no one knew for certain who had won. Soon after the battle the rumours began. It was reliably reported that, on certain nights, ghostly soldiers could be seen re-enacting the combat. So persistent did these rumours become that the King sent a team of his officers to investigate. Colonel Lewis Kirke, Captain Dudley, Captain Wainman and three others submitted their report: here is part of that report exactly as they wrote it nearly three and a half centuries ago.

THE BATTLE OF EDGE HILL

Col. Lewis Kirk

Edge Hill, in the very confines of Warwickshire, near unto Keynton, in Northamptonshire, a place, as appears by the sequel, destined for civil wars and battles; as where King John fought a battle with his barons, and where, in defence of the kingdom's laws and liberty, was fought a bloody conflict between His Majesty's and the Parliament's forces. At this Edge Hill, at the very place where the battle was fought, have since, and doth appear, strange and portentous apparitions of two jarring and contrary armies, as I shall in order deliver, it being certified by men of most credit in those parts, as William Wood, Esquire, Samuel Marshall, Minister, and others, on Saturday, which was in Christmas time . . . Between twelve and one o'clock in the morning was heard by some shepherds, and other countrymen, and travellers, first the sound of drums far off, and the noise of soldiers, as it were, giving out their last groans; at which they were much amazed, and stood still, till it seemed, by the nearness of the noise, to approach them; at which, too much affrighted, they sought to withdraw as fast as they possibly could; but then, on the sudden, whilst they were in their cogitations, appeared in the air the same incorporeal soldiers that made those clamours, and immediately, with ensigns displayed, drums beating, muskets going off, cannons discharged, horses neighing, which also to these men were visible, the alarum or entrance to this game of death was, one army, which gave the first charge, having the King's colours, and the other the Parliament's, at their head or front of the battle, and so pell-mell to it they went. The King's forces seemed at first to have the best, but afterwards to be put into apparent rout. But till two or three in the morning in equal scale continued this dreadful fight, the clattering of arms, noise of cannons, cries of soldiers, so amazing and terrifying that poor men, they could not believe they were mortal, or give credit to their eyes and ears; run away they durst not, for fear of being made a prey to these infernal soldiers, and so they, with much fear and affright, stayed to behold the success of the business, which at last suited to this effect. After some hours' fight, that army which carried the King's colours withdrew, or rather appeared to fly; the other remaining, as it were, masters of the field, stayed a good space triumphing, and expressing all the signs of joy and conquest, and then, with all their drums, trumpets, ordnance, and soldiers, vanished.

The poor men, glad that they were gone that had so long stayed them there against their wills, made with haste to Keynton, and there knocking up Mr Wood, a Justice of the Peace, who called up his neighbour, Mr Marshall, the Minister, they gave them an account of the whole passage, and averred it upon their oaths to be true. At which affirmation of theirs, being much amazed, they should hardly have given credit to it, but would have conjectured the men to have been either mad or drunk, had they not known some of them to have been of approved integrity; and so, suspending their judgements till the next night about the same hour, they, with the same men, and all the substantial inhabitants of that and the neighbouring parishes drew thither; where,

about half an hour after their arrival, on Sunday, being Christmas night, appeared in the same tumultuous warlike manner, the same two adverse armies, fighting with as much spite and spleen as formerly; and so departed the gentlemen and all the spectators, much terrified with these visions of horror, withdrawing themselves to their houses, beseeching God to defend them from those hellish and prodigious enemies. The next night they appeared not, nor all that week, so that the dwellers thereabout were in good hope they had for ever departed. But on the ensuing Saturday night, in the same place, and at the same hour, they were again seen with far greater tumult, fighting in the manner aforementioned, for four hours, or very near, and then vanished. Appearing again on Sunday night, and performing the same actions of hostility and bloodshed, so that Mr Wood and others, whose faith, it should seem, was not strong enough to carry them out against these delusions, forsook their habitations thereabout, and retired themselves to other more secure dwellings; but Mr Marshall stayed, and some other; and so successively the next Saturday and Sunday the same tumults and prodigious sights and actions were put in the state and condition they were formerly.

An interesting story though hardly true you may think, but then why should such reputable people *invent* such a tale? They certainly believed in what they had seen, as indeed do some people today who, when they have visited Edge Hill at night, claim to have heard, if not actually seen the warring armies.

There are many tales of unquiet spirits returning to places known to them. Like the soldiers of Edge Hill, some are said

to appear to this very day. Bisham Abbey in Buckinghamshire is now the home of the National Sports Centre where many young people enjoy sports coaching sessions, but the building has a tragic story. The guilty and remorseful spirit of Lady Hobby is still said to pace the corridors of her former home. Like Lady Macbeth, she can never cleanse herself of the blood of an innocent victim.

THE GHOST OF LADY HOBBY

Sybil Marshall

In the days of the first Queen Elizabeth, there lived at Bisham Abbey a proud and beautiful lady. She was proud of her face and figure, proud of her beautiful clothes and jewels, proud of her own ancient lineage and that of the man into whose family she had married. In fact, she was proud of everything except her little son, the next Hobby in the line. Of him she could not be proud, for though he was as healthy and sturdy a little boy as any mother could have wished, the truth was that he was a dullard at his lessons, and seemed not to be able to learn at all.

This grieved his proud mother beyond all reason. She simply could not understand how it could possibly be that a son of hers should not be as good at his books as he was bright and skilful at his outdoor games and sports. She made up her mind, after trying many tutors for him, to teach him herself; for it seemed plain to her that the reason for his backwardness was that he would not, and not that he could not, learn. Very well, he should be made to learn, and if he did not, then he should be severely punished with strap and rod. She herself would be his mentor, and nothing should prevail upon her to relent until her son was as much the equal of his peers in learning as he was in every other gentlemanly pursuit.

So poor Hobby's ordeal began. Day after day he sat at his lessons with his stern mother as tutor, while the Thames ran sweetly through the meadows of his prison, and his friends played and fished there in the sunshine. For every failure, the hours of his schooling were lengthened; for every mistake, extra work was given; for every disobedience, the rod or the strap were applied without mercy, in order to make him try harder, and do better.

Deprived of his outdoor life, he began to grow wan and listless. Faced with more and more work that he could not comprehend, and of an amount he could not accomplish, he appeared every day to be more dull than he had been the day before. Fear of failure, and of punishment, robbed him of what skill and understanding he had; and still his cold, proud mother saw it only as an insult to her that he would not do better.

The pen was his chief enemy. Try as he would, he could not complete a single line of his copy-book without the ink spirtling from the end of his quill, without blots dropping on to his work, without smudges from his inky fingers or his cuffs as his hand laboriously crept along the line of writing. For every blot, for every smudge, there was a swift cut with the cane, so that his tears ran down to complete the ruin of his copy-book page.

There came a day when poor young Hobby did worse than usual, and his tutor lost all the remains of her maternal patience. Seizing him, she began to beat him with all the pent-up rage of her proud, frustrated feelings. His screams fell on deaf ears, his pleas for clemency went unheeded. Tirelessly her arm rose and fell, till the child at last fell senseless at her feet. Whether he died there and then, or a few hours later, as a result of her attack, nobody knows. Nobody knows, either, the extent of her grief and remorse, when the full horror of her treatment of Hobby came home to her; but that she died in the course of time, and could find no solace or forgiveness even in the grave, is proved by her wandering, unquiet spirit, which paces still through the house, and lingers longest in the room where Hobby was beaten to death for nothing more than the blotting of his copy-book.

Many are the people who have testified to seeing the ghost of his cruel mother, for it is no ordinary ghost. Down the corridor she glides, dressed in the full gown of Elizabethan fashion, with stomacher and ruff, coif, weeds and wimple; but the sight of her is enough to chill the blood, for the dark stuff of her heavy dress gleams up as ghastly white, while face, ruff and trimmings show black against them. As for her hands, they are the most terrible of all. Stretched always in front of her, the black hands strive in vain to reach and plunge themselves into the cleansing water of a wash-bowl, also black, that floats in mid-air at arm's length before her. Try as she may, she cannot get near it, for it sways this way and that of its own accord, keeping always just out of her reach.

Perhaps the reversal of the tones in the apparition is a constant reminder of the unnatural behaviour of a mother towards her own small child. And as for the bowl, what horrors of the scene at Bisham Abbey in the immediate aftermath of the child's cruel death does it not conjure up!

Lest this should be regarded as yet another macabre tale 'invented by the folk' from very scanty evidence, there exists something more concrete than Lady Hobby's remorseful spirit to vouch for a little of the truth of it.

Some hundred and twenty years ago, repairs were being carried out at the ancient house. In the room in which the dull little scholar sat so often in tears at his lessons, it was necessary to remove the shutters from a window. Tucked down between the shutter and the wall, the workmen discovered several copy-books of the kind that children of the past were so wont to pore over in distress. All dated back to the days of Elizabeth the First; and one of them corresponded in every way with the sad cause of little Hobby's fate, for in it there was not one single line which was not inked, and blotted, and smudged, and finally washed with painful tears.

Inside the stories

For discussion

The stories in this section are all to do with things that happened in particular places. Think about your own local area and the country round about, and share any stories that are linked with it. There may seem very little at first, but almost certainly further talk and investigation will reveal stories about local buildings or places that are said to be haunted, about nearby rocks or hills that are associated with weird or magical happenings, and stories told against people from other towns or villages, or from across the county border, and so on. You may find it helps to have a map of your town and a local ordnance survey map handy, as the sight of names and places often triggers off memories of stories connected with them.

On your own

1 Extend your research into local tales by asking adults for any stories they know which are connected with the area they now live in or with the area their families come from. Older adults are often a good source and you may be able to write down stories in their own words as they tell them. You may find that some of the stories are quite recent – for example, they may be associated with the last war, or with unexpected happenings when the new motorway was cut through the country, or with phantom figures or vehicles that appear on local roads.

There are vast numbers of similar 'local' stories from around the world and you may be able to collect stories about the spirit of the place from the Caribbean, Africa, India . . . or from just about anywhere.

If you are very lucky, you could make a tape-recording of an adult telling such a story. In any case, the important thing is to get down the details somehow so that you can retell the story yourself in a convincing way.

2 Go to your local library and find out about any local stories and legends. Often, small books published by local historians tell of such things. You may find that a local bookshop has a stock of publications with titles like *Ghosts of –shire*. It isn't only country areas that are rich in such tales: London and the inner cities are full of ghosts, and beneath their pavements lie ancient churches, long-buried temples and palaces, docks and wharves, playhouses and places of execution, many with stories to tell.

Share your findings and then produce a collection of stories as a booklet or as a display of material.

3 Write your own story on The Spirit of the Place that could be included in this section. You could work your story up from the local material you have already discovered or you could invent a totally new story from your own imagination. If you do the latter, you will need to think carefully about finding a setting that has some history associated with it – a church or an old inn, or an isolated house, perhaps; or it might be a local landmark such as a curiously shaped hill or a rock. Think about what might have happened there, to whom it happened and why it happened. Think about how people today regard the story.

As a group

The story of 'The Wedding at Stanton Drew' would make a powerful play. Think of the group of merry revellers enjoying their dance after the wedding; the quarrel between the bride and the musician; the appearance of the mysterious piper; the terrible dance that begins in joy and ends in horror; the whole group turning to stone. Pick out the dialogue you need and improvise where necessary. Although the story is an old one, you could set the story in modern times and play suitable music. Find yourselves two musicians or use a recording to mime to and – away you go into the dance.

3
TALL STORIES

Most of us tend to exaggerate, to stretch the truth a little from time to time. It might be to make ourselves look better, or braver, or more successful than we really are. Fishermen, as we all know, are supposed to find it difficult to resist telling about the enormous fish that they caught but that broke free just at the last moment – the one that got away. Many of us invent stories to get out of being blamed for things, or to excuse ourselves – 'My sister's gerbil ate my homework, Miss, and made it into a beautiful nest of shredded paper.' And what do teachers and parents say when they don't believe a word of it? Why, they say, 'Don't tell stories . . . Don't make things up.'

What's the best excuse *you* ever heard? Discuss it in pairs, and, if you don't know one, you can make one up. Share your ideas.

However far-fetched your tall story excuses, probably none of them is as unlikely as this builder's request to his boss for sick leave which just *might* be true. Certainly it is possible . . .

TALL STORY

Jean L'Anselme, trans. Michael Benedikt

Dear Sir,

By the time I arrived at the house where you sent me to make repairs, the storm had torn a good fifty bricks from the roof. So I set up on the roof of the building a beam and a pulley and I hoisted up a couple of baskets of bricks. When I had finished repairing the building there were a lot of bricks left over since I had brought up more than I needed and also because there were some bad, reject bricks that I still had left to bring down. I hoisted the basket back up again and hitched up the line at the bottom. Then I climbed back up again and filled up the basket with the extra bricks. Then I went down to the bottom and untied the line. Unfortunately, the basket of bricks was much heavier than I was and before I knew what was happening, the basket started to plunge down, lifting me suddenly off the ground. I decided to keep my grip and hang on, realising that to let go would end in disaster – but halfway up I ran into the basket coming down and received a severe blow on the shoulder. I then continued to the top, banging my head against the beam and getting my fingers jammed in the pulley. When the basket hit the ground it burst its bottom, allowing all the bricks to spill out. Since I was now heavier than the basket I started back down again at high speed. Halfway down, I met the basket coming up, and received several severe injuries on my shins. When I hit the ground, I landed on the bricks, getting several more painful cuts and bruises from the sharp edges.

At this moment I must have lost my presence of mind, because I let go of the line. The basket came down again, giving me another heavy blow on the head, and putting me in the hospital. I respectfully request sick leave.

Perhaps the best retelling of this story is the version recorded by Gerard Hoffnung many years ago in a speech to students in Oxford. Fortunately, it is still available on an audio cassette – *Hoffnung: Speech at the Oxford Union, December 1958* – published by BBC Enterprises. If you get a chance, do listen to this master storyteller at work, and enjoy not only the story but the timing and the skill with which Hoffnung controls his audience.

Storytellers are all liars, though some tell more outrageous lies than others – and they are the tellers of tall stories. At the heart of the tall story is an out-and-out lie told with an absolutely straight face for the pure pleasure of it. The audience listens wide-eyed, half hoping the tale is true, half knowing it is a complete invention. Have *you* heard of the skyscraper so tall they had to put hinges on the top two floors to let the moon go by? And what about the pancakes so thin they only had one side, or the hen that laid eggs with the date printed on them?

One of the best modern storytellers – some say he is *the* best – is Eamon Kelly from Ireland. Although the Irish have a great many stories so tall you might lean over backwards and crack your skull on the pavement before you would see the tops of them, the story Eamon Kelly tells here is not so much tall as very, very deep . . .

THE HOUSE UNDER THE SEA

Eamon Kelly

I remember one time I was talking to a man from the seaside, and he told me he was one day down by the strand and he came across a young seal, and he caught him and put him in a bag and brought him home and threw him under the table.

There was a crowd of the neighbours in that night playing cards, and around ten o'clock they heard someone below on the strand and he calling:

'Timmie. Where are you, Timmie?'

They went out and down to the strand, thinking maybe that there was some boatman in trouble, but when they went down they couldn't see anyone. It was a fine bright moonlight night. They doubled back to the house and they were no sooner inside than they heard the call again:

'Timmie. Where are you, Timmie?'

Well, they couldn't make hog, dog nor devil of it. It wasn't the voice of anyone they knew. They opened the door wide and the call came nearer:

'Timmie. Do you hear me, Timmie? Why don't you come out to me?'

They looked from one to the other, changing colour, and one man said:

'Who's Timmie?'

'I'm Timmie,' says the seal under the table, 'and that's my brother Johnny calling me!'

I tell you they weren't long lifting up the bag, opening the mouth of it, putting it outside the door and saying:

'Well, if you're Timmie, off with you to Johnny. And don't be putting the heart crossways in us!'

'Would you believe that!' says the man from the seaside.

'Why wouldn't I believe it!' says I, 'when I had a far more remarkable experience myself.' And I told him the story exactly as I am going to tell it to you now.

I am a stone mason by trade, I began, and it was the time we were building the pier in Ballinskelligs, and I was this day walking down by the sea when a man came along in a boat.

'Will you come for a drive?' says he.

'I will,' says I.

'Get in,' says he.

And I did. He had a gun in the bottom of the boat and when we were gone awhile we saw something black bobbing in the water. 'A seal,' says he, taking aim and as he fired the seal ducked. We pulled over to the place and wasn't there a pool of blood on top of the waves.

'Ah ha,' says he, 'I knew I hit him. We'll hold on here now for a while and that seal will float up on the tide to us.'

We threw out the anchor and waited, but if we were there yet the seal wouldn't float. The sea was turning rough, the horses shaking their white manes, and it looked like as if we were in for squalls, so we said we would move on. The man went to pull the anchor but if the cat went a pound he couldn't knock a shake out of it.

'Play tough,' says I, 'and I'll go down to see what's holding it.' A very foolish remark too, now that I come to think of it!

'Be cautious!' says he.

And I came out of the coat and handed him my hat, took a deep breath and down with me, and I thought I'd never come to the end of the chain it was so long. With that, my toe struck something solid. I looked down and where was the hook of the anchor, curled in under the lintel of a door! I hopped off on the ground and where was I? Standing in front of a long, low, thatched, whitewashed house.

'Come on away in,' says someone talking inside.

I straightened my tie and faced in and the man of the house got up to welcome me, and I noticed that he was wearing a bandage around his head.

'Is it anyone hit you?' says I, all concern.

'You should know that,' says he, 'or that specimen that was in the boat with you. Only for I ducking so quick he'd have let the daylight into my brains! And isn't it a fright,' says he, 'that a man can't put his nose out for a puff of air without someone having a cork at him, or is there any law or order in the world above?'

'Well now,' says I, 'I'm not a shooting man myself.'

'Nor you haven't the cut of it,' he said. 'I've only to look at you, you wouldn't hurt a fly. Take a chair and sit down. You must be starved with the hunger.'

And 'twas true for him. A spell in the salt air and you would chew ivy after it. His wife, a small, compact little woman, was there too, very busy over the fire.

'Close out the door one of ye,' says she, 'the wind is turning the smoke on me.'

The door was banged out, sweeping the anchor before it. Up it flew and there was I cut off from the world above. A nice predicament to be in!

'Don't you fret,' says the man of the house. 'You can stay the night with us. We'll fix up a shakedown, some place for you! Woman,' says he then calling the wife, 'take up the eggs or we'll have to get hammers to 'em.'

The table was laid for the supper so we all sat over, the man and his wife, his four sons and his three daughters, and talk of hospitality, they did not know what to make of me. 'Shove up the bread to the man . . . pass down the milk . . . will you have another egg . . . don't be sparing 'em . . . eat your fill . . . and let tomorrow take care of itself.' Such nice people, and so freemaking! You'd cover a lot of ground to-day before you would meet their likes.

And not like here they wouldn't be one minute idle. No sooner was the table cleared and the ware washed than the mother and the daughters were carding and spinning wool, and the sons were drawing in sheafs of oats and scotching them on the backs of chairs, and the old man, sore and all as the head was by him, turned in to pointing scolbs* and 'twas plain that they would be putting a new coat of thatch on the house in the morning, which they were first thing after the breakfast.

I knocked out in the yard. It was in the settle bed near the fire I spent the night. Oh, it was so comfortable, it was like a wren's nest. I knocked out in the yard as I said, and after throwing my eye along the roof I said to the man of the house:

'Blessed hour tonight, what happened to your chimney stack?'

'Well,' says he, 'like everyone else around here, 'tis a wickerwork one I had, made of rods, and I pulled it down for 'twas rotten.'

'Well now,' says I, 'if you can get the loan of a mason's traps you have a man standing here on the sod that'll have a stone chimney stack up for you while you'd be winking.'

'I hear,' says he, 'They're the coming thing.'

'If you had an air to that,' says I, 'You could sing it.'

So he went away and he got a trowel, hammer and plumb rule. He drew stones, got lime and sand and made mortar, and I fell into work and in no time at all I had the new chimney stack built, with a nice projecting ledge and a saw-toothed slate all round the flue to keep the jackdaws from perching on it,

*split and pointed rods for thatching

for no word of a lie they can be an awful nuisance. I looked down then and the yard was full of seal people all very taken by the new chimney stack, and every man of them wanting one of the self same pattern on top of his own house. So I went away building chimney stacks till I lost all track of time.

Then one morning I said to the man of the house:

'I wonder will I ever again see the world above?'

'What a hurry you're in,' says he, 'are you getting tired of us?'

'Ah, 'tisn't that at all,' I said, 'but they'll be wondering where I am at home.'

'Well in that case,' says he, 'you can go to-day. Woman,' he called to his wife, 'where is my overcoat?'

She brought it and he put it on, and he looked like a seal now. I hopped up on his back and he made one spring and shot up through the waves and in two shakes he had me in above at Cuas a 'Mhadra Uisge. I thanked him, and looked around and there wasn't a sinner in view. I moved up on the high ground and I saw all the cars above around the chapel.

''Tis Sunday,' says I, 'and the people are inside at Mass.'

I ran up and I was just into the porch in time to hear myself being prayed for from the altar!

Creid é no ná creid tá sé sin fíor!*

*Believe it or not that is true!

Travellers' tales brought back by voyagers and explorers were an early form of tall story. They were listened to eagerly, told and retold, and grew more outlandish with every telling. Sir John Mandeville's book, *Travels*, published over six hundred years ago, contains a strange collection of such stories, and tells of:

folk of great stature, as they were giants, horrible and foul to the sight; and they have but one eye, and that is in the midst of the forehead. . . In another isle are men without heads; and their eyes and their mouths are behind their shoulders . . . Yet there is another isle where the folk have but one foot, and that foot is so broad it will cover all the body and ombre [shade] it from the sun. And upon this foot they will run so fast it is a wonder to see.

Think of the amazement that was felt when travellers first set eyes on a hippopotamus, a rhino, a gorilla, a giraffe or a whale, and what stories might have grown around them. It is said that stories of mermaids grew from sightings of seals, and that the most beautiful of all imagined creatures, the unicorn, was conjured up from people finding the single ivory tusk of the narwhal cast up on the seashore. We know the truth now, but mermaids and unicorns still appear in children's stories – perhaps because we would like to believe in them, if only a little.

Now we know so much about the world. Every day the television camera brings the strange and amazing straight into our homes. So we look further afield for our weird and wonderful tall stories. We imagine creatures from outer space, flying saucers bearing aliens who may have delightful, or not so delightful, ways. We imagine whole new worlds and civilisations light years away, and we invent space travellers who boldly go and bring us back the stories we crave. We enjoy the little thrill of terror, the shiver of the unexpected or strange. But above all, we cannot bear a gap, a mystery – we have to fill it with a story.

Such stories have been around for a long time. The Greek writer, Lucian, who was born about AD120, wrote a *Veracious History*, telling of imaginary travels which took him as far as the moon itself. This is his description of the moon's inhabitants as he imagined them. They live in a place very different from the dusty, airless and barren globe that we now know the moon to be.

MOON PEOPLE
Lucian
trans. Paul Turner

When Moon people grow old, they do not die. They just vanish into
thin air, like smoke – and talking of smoke, I must tell you about
their diet, which is precisely the same for everyone. When they feel
hungry, they light a fire and roast some frogs on it – for there are
lots of these creatures flying about in the air. Then, while the frogs
are roasting, they draw up chairs round the fire, as if it were a sort of
dining-room table, and gobble up the smoke.

This is all they ever eat, and to quench their thirst they just
squeeze some air into a glass and drink that: the liquid produced is
rather like dew.

Bald men are considered very handsome on the Moon, and long
hair is thought absolutely revolting; but on young stars like the
Comets, which have not yet lost their hair, it is just the other way
round – or so at least I was told by a Comet-dweller who was having
a holiday on the Moon when I was there.

I forgot to mention that they wear their beards a little above the
knee; and they have not any toenails, for the very good reason that
they have not any toes. What they have got, however, is a large
cabbage growing just above the buttocks like a tail. It is always in
flower, and never gets broken, even if they fall flat on their backs.

When they blow their noses, what comes out is extremely sour
honey, and when they have been working hard or taking strenuous
exercise, they sweat milk at every pore. Occasionally they turn it into
cheese by adding a few drops of the honey. They also make olive oil
out of onions, and the resulting fluid is extremely rich and has a very
delicate perfume.

They have any number of vines, which produce not wine but
water, for the grapes are made of ice; and there, in my view, you

have the scientific explanation of hailstorms, which occur whenever the wind is strong enough to blow the fruit off those vines.

They use their stomachs as handbags for carrying things around in, for they can open and shut them at will. If you look inside one, there is nothing to be seen in the way of digestive organs, but the whole interior is lined with fur so that it can also be used as a centrally-heated pram for babies in cold weather.

The upper classes wear clothes made of flexible glass, but this material is rather expensive, so most people have to be content with copper textiles – for there is any amount of copper in the soil, which becomes as soft as wool when soaked in water.

I hardly like to tell you about their eyes, for fear you should think I am exaggerating, because it really does sound almost incredible. Still, I might as well risk it, so here goes: their eyes are detachable, so that you can take them out when you do not want to see anything and put them back when you do. Needless to say, it is not unusual to find someone who has mislaid his own eyes altogether and is always having to borrow someone else's; and those who can afford it keep quite a number of spare pairs by them, just in case. As for ears, the Tree-men have wooden ones of their own, and everyone else has to be satisfied with a couple of plane-tree leaves instead.

I must just mention one other thing I saw in the King's palace. It was a large mirror suspended over a fairly shallow tank. If you got into the tank, you could hear everything that was being said on the Earth, and if you looked in the mirror, you could see what was going on anywhere in the world, as clearly as if you were actually there yourself. I had a look at all the people I knew at home, but whether they saw me or not I really cannot say.

Well, that is what it is like on the Moon. If you do not believe me, go and see for yourself.

Inside the story

In pairs

Imagine how Lucian might have described other aspects of Moon people's lives. For example, how do they sleep? What are their occupations? What do they do for entertainment? Do they have schools for their children – if so, what are they like? How do they show they are happy or sad? What are their transport systems like? Do they go shopping and, if so, what things do they like to buy? . . . There are dozens of things we don't know from Lucian's account. Choose one aspect of moon people's lives and jot down your ideas about it.

Work up your jottings into a paragraph, telling the story in the same chatty style as Lucian. You may find it helpful to use some of the phrases that appear in the original, such as 'I forgot to mention . . .', or 'I hardly like to tell you about . . .', or 'I must tell you about. . .'. And, like Lucian, you can use his trick of saying that you are worried that people might think you are exaggerating, but . . .

Read over what you have written and practise telling it as a story to your partner.

As a group

I Tell your bit of the story to the rest of the group, trying to make it as convincing as possible. Think first about how you will get their attention, about the tone of voice you will need to use if you are to be believed, about how you must look your listeners in the eye if you are to be convincing.

2 Put all your individual paragraphs and drawings together as a complete description – as a handwritten or word-processed illustrated booklet, or as a wall display.

On your own

I You have read how Sir John Mandeville's book of *Travels* described the strange, one-footed creature that was reported to exist and you can see the old illustration of it on p. 29. The other pictures show other strange creatures that early travellers said they had seen. Choose one and describe it in detail, saying where it lives, what it does, what it eats, what its habits are, and so on. If you can make your description sound as if it was written several centuries ago, using the kind of language to be found in *Travels*, so much the better.

2 Write your own description of imaginary people from some other planet – Mars, Venus or Pluto, for example. Make sure you exaggerate in the same way as Lucian. When you have written your paragraph, draw a picture to illustrate it.

Perhaps the most famous teller of tall tales was a German called Rudolph Erich Raspe who was born in 1737. You have probably never heard of him, but you may well have heard of Baron Munchausen, the character he created. Raspe was an untrustworthy rascal who was continually in debt and embezzled money from the Duke of Hesse-Cassel. When he was found out, he fled to England, and it was in England – and in English – that *The Adventures of Baron Munchausen* first appeared in print. These amazing stories were first published in 1785 and were an immediate success. People loved them and they have been read for two hundred years. In fact, two centuries after he first appeared in print, a film was made of some of the Baron's adventures. It is available as a video and you may have a chance to see it.

Was there a real Baron Munchausen? Apparently, yes. He was born in 1720, was a hunter and a soldier who fought for the Russians against the Turks, and was famous for his tall stories.

Just as he made free with other people's money, Raspe wasn't above stealing someone else's good story and embroidering it in his own way. Lucian's tale of the Moon people was well known to Raspe and, not surprisingly, he thought it good enough to give to Baron Munchausen as one of *his* stories.

At the beginning of each chapter of Baron Munchausen's Adventures, Raspe gave a brief summary of what it contained. Here is a summary for one chapter of the book:

A Voyage to Russia in which the Baron Proves Himself a Good Shot – He Loses His Horse, and Finds a Wolf – Makes Him Draw His Sledge – Enjoys Himself at St Petersburg, Where He Meets a Distinguished General.

Before you read the chapter, discuss what you think might be in it. Remember, the Baron was supposed to be a really great liar.

Now read on, and find how close you were to the 'truth'.

A Voyage To Russia

Rudolph Erich Raspe

I set off on a journey to Russia, in the midst of winter, from a just notion that frost and snow must of course mend the roads, which every traveller had described as uncommonly bad through the northern parts of Germany, Poland, Courland, and Livonia. I went on horseback, as it is the most convenient manner of travelling, provided, however, that rider and horse are in good condition.

I was lightly clothed, and I felt the inconvenience of this the more I advanced north-east. What must not a poor old man have suffered in that severe weather and climate, whom I saw on a bleak common in Poland, lying on the road, helpless, shivering, and hardly having wherewithal to cover his nakedness! I pitied the poor soul. Though I felt the severity of the air myself, I threw my mantle over him, and immediately I heard a voice from the heavens, blessing me for that piece of charity, saying –

'The devil take me, my son, if this good action does not receive its reward.'

I went on: night and darkness overtook me. No village was in sight. The country was covered with snow, and I was unacquainted with the road.

Tired, I alighted, and fastened my horse to something like a pointed stump of a tree, which appeared above the snow; for the sake of safety, I placed my pistols under my arm, and laid down on the snow, where I slept so soundly that I did not open my eyes till full daylight. It is not easy to conceive my astonishment when I found myself in the midst of a village, lying in a churchyard; my horse was nowhere to be seen, but soon I heard him neigh somewhere above me. On looking upwards, I beheld him hanging by his bridle from the weathercock of the steeple. Matters were now very plain to me: the village had been covered with snow; a sudden change of weather had taken place overnight; I had sunk down to the churchyard whilst asleep, gently, and in the same proportion as the snow had melted away; and what in the dark I had taken to be a stump of a little tree appearing above the snow, to which I had tied my horse, proved to have been the cross or weathercock of the steeple!

Without long consideration, I took one of my pistols, shot the bridle in two, brought down the horse, and proceeded on my journey.

All went well until we advanced into the interior parts of Russia, where I found travelling on horseback rather unfashionable in winter; therefore I submitted, as I always do, to the custom of the country, took a single horse sledge, and drove briskly towards St. Petersburg. I do not exactly recollect whether it was in Eastland or Jugemanland, but I remember that, in the midst of a dreary forest, I spied a terrible wolf making after me, with all the speed of ravenous winter hunger.

He soon overtook me. There was no possibility of escape. Mechanically I laid myself down flat in the sledge, and let my horse run for our safety. What I wished, but hardly hoped or expected, happened immediately after. The wolf paid no attention to me in the least, but leaping over me, and falling furiously on the horse, began instantly to tear and devour the hind part of the poor animal, which ran the faster for his pain and terror. Thus unnoticed and safe myself, I lifted my head slily up, and with horror I beheld that the wolf had eaten his way into the horse's body. It was not long before he had fairly forced himself into it, when I took my advantage, and fell upon him with the butt end of my whip. This unexpected attack in his rear frightened him so much, that he leaped forward with all his might: the horse's carcase dropped on the ground; but in his place the wolf was in the harness, and I on my part whipping him continually, we both arrived safe at St. Petersburg, contrary to our respective expectations, and very much to the astonishment of the spectators.

It was some time before I could obtain a commission in the army, and for several months I sported away my time and money in the most gentleman-like manner.

I passed many a night in play and drinking. The coldness of the climate and the customs of the nation make drinking a matter of more social importance than it is in our sober Germany; and I have found in Russia some people of the highest reputation most accomplished in this practice. But we were all wretched fellows compared to an old general, with a grizzled moustache and a bronzed skin, who dined with us at the table d'hôte.

In a battle with the Turks this brave fellow lost the top of his skull, so that every time a stranger was introduced to him he excused himself, with the greatest courtesy in the world, for wearing his hat at table. He was in the habit of consuming at dinner several glasses of brandy, and as a wind-up he would empty a flask of rum, occasionally doubling the dose, according to circumstances. Nevertheless it was impossible to discover in him any signs of intoxication. The matter is puzzling, no doubt, and it was a long time before I was able to understand it, until one day, by chance, I discovered the explanation of the mystery. The general was in the habit of raising his hat from time to time. I had often noticed it, but paid no attention to the fact; for it was nothing surprising that his head should feel warm and in need of a little cool air. But finally I perceived that every time he raised his hat he lifted the silver plate, which was fixed so as to serve instead of the top of his head, and then the fumes of various liquors which he had drunk passed off in light vapours. Thus was the mystery unravelled: I recounted this discovery to two of my friends, and offered to prove its correctness.

I placed myself with my pipe behind the general; and the moment he raised his hat, I lit a piece of paper for my pipe. We then enjoyed a spectacle most novel and surprising. I had changed into a column of fire the column of smoke which ascended from the general's head, and the vapours which chanced to be caught in the old man's hair looked like a bluish halo of a brilliance surpassing any which has circled the head of the greatest saint. This experiment did not remain unknown to the general; he was so amiable about it that he permitted us to repeat the practice which gave him so venerable an air.

Inside the stories

In pairs

Here is the summary for another chapter from *The Adventures of Baron Munchausen*:

Desperate Encounter Between the Baron's Nose and a Door-Post, with Its Wonderful Effects – Ten Ducks and Other Fowl Killed with One Shot – Further Successes, and Triumphal Return Home – Numerous Anecdotes of the Chase (hunting).

From what you know of the Baron's character, discuss what you think the chapter might contain.

On your own

When you have talked about some of the more outlandish possibilities, either write your own version of one or two of the episodes in the chapter outlined above or imagine some of your own. For example, The Baron meets a lion; The Baron learns to fly; The Baron demonstrates his amazing strength.

As a group

Put selections of your new episodes together to make whole new strings of stories that Baron Munchausen might have wished he had told. Make a wall display of them, with suitable illustrations, or bring them all together as a booklet using the word processor.

Modern Munchausens?

1 Imagine a character today who enjoys spinning tall stories like those told by the Baron and by Eamon Kelly. It might be a grown-up – a parent, aunt, uncle, grandparent – who enjoys telling such stories to entertain children. Perhaps they are bedtime stories. Or it might be a person who sits in the pub and tells stories to amaze his or her friends at the bar. It might even be a small child or someone your own age who simply can't help 'telling stories'. Of course, you may not have to imagine a person like this – you may actually *know* someone who is a natural tall story teller. Think carefully about your character. What does he or she look like? Write a paragraph describing the person. Describe the setting, the audience, how the stories are told, and write a tall story that your character might have told.

2 Stories are for telling. When you have developed your modern tall stories, commit the main ideas to memory and *tell* them to the rest of the group. Speak slowly and don't forget to include lots of small, convincing details so that your listeners can build up pictures in their mind's eye.

3 Some papers and magazines even rely on invented stories to entertain and amuse their readers. LONDON BUS FOUND ON MOON! screams the headline, or it may be GIANT CABBAGE ATE MY SON!, or even ALIENS INDOCTRINATE OUR KIDS – TEN WAYS TO TELL IF YOUR TEACHER IS A MARTIAN. (Actually, we invented the last two but the first one is genuine.) Make up your own 'tall story' headline and write the accompanying story.

SECTION B:
INSIDE STORIES

1
TRICKSTERS AND RIDDLERS

People seem to like stories about tricks and riddles. For centuries they have been told all over the world in many different languages. Although the characters and the settings may be different, the stories are often very similar whether they come from India, Africa, the Caribbean or from Russia, or whether they are traditional tales from the British Isles. It is not surprising this should be so. Good stories like these get around. They are borrowed and are passed down over the years; they are worn smooth and comfortable with the telling. They come easily to the tongue for they are, above all, stories to be told and retold. And they live on, partly because they entertain and partly because they often contain some grains of wisdom and truth.

1

2

3

4

5

Anancy, the Spiderman, is the hero of scores of Afro-Caribbean stories. Anancy began life in West Africa as the Ashanti Spider God. Africans who were transported as slaves to the Caribbean Islands of the West Indies took his stories with them. The Caribbean writer, James Berry, who has collected many of the Anancy tales, says Anancy is, 'Sly and soft voiced, he can be anything from a lovable rogue to an artful prince. Often, he gets overwhelmed by a terrible greed he cannot help. Essentially both a spider and a man,

his nature allows him to change as the situation demands.' Anancy is godlike, but he also has a fair share of low cunning and often manages to overcome superior strength by his clever tricks.

James Berry, who retells the story here, writes that he is thankful to his parents 'for keeping their links with the stories and for passing them on to us in our Jamaican village, out in moonlight or in dim paraffin lamplight, during rain and storm winds, through empty-belly times or big bellyfuls.'

TIGER AND ANANCY MEET FI WAR

Tiger sen Anancy a messige that him comin roun him house to kill him. Anancy sen back messige tellin Tiger to come. Come any way he like. Bring all him friend them with him. For him Anancy will have all him friend them with him.

Tiger arrive. Tiger come like king on horseback, man, with weapon them, with a crowd of Tiger-man them around him. And every man carry weapon of differen kind.

Tiger and him friend them stop there at Anancy yard-gate. Them stop there, man. Them see only one frien with Anancy in the middle of the yard. Them see nobody else. Them see that Bro Nancy has no

weapon. Them see his frien Bro Dog has no weapon either. Them see Anancy lying down with him head on a trunk-piece of wood.

Them stan there at the gate. Bro Tiger and the Tiger-man them jus stan there in puzzlement. Them wonder what trick that Anancy planned. Them dohn know what move to make.

Hear the Anancy now, loud-loud,

'Come on Bro Tiger. Come on. Don't torture me. Come and chop off my head. Let the world know you are a brave-brave man. Let my head drop like a block of wood.'

Tiger feel a fool. Him sit on the horse with him head all confuse. Listen him now,

'Bro Nancy. You know I have no intention to kill you. Why make you mistrus me?'

Hear Anancy,

'Come on Bro Tiger. Dohn stretch out you brave deed to uncall-for torturin. Come and do what you come to do. If you dohn do it today you only have to do it tomorrow.'

'Bro Nancy,' Tiger say, pleadin, 'you know I not that sort of man. You know that.'

And Tiger get down from him horse. Tiger give up him weapon them to the Tiger-man them. Hear Tiger,

'I comin, Bro Nancy. I comin to shake hands with you. I wahn the whole worl to know we good-good friends.'

Hear Anancy,

'If you say so Bro Tiger. If you say so.' Then listen how the Anancy wrap up him word them in tricky traps. 'You invite youself to my yard, I dohn say, go away. You wahn to shake my hand, I dohn say, oh no.'

Bro Tiger come step through Bro Nancy yard-gate. Bro Tiger sink. Bro Tiger fall straight down in a pit concealed with dry leaves and have rock them at the bottom.

Every Tiger-man get a bad-bad shake-up. Every one come cluster roun the pit. Every one work and work to get Tiger out.

Bro Tiger get lift out. Him get lift out all battered with limbs broke-up.

Anancy and Dog dohn wait to see the Tiger-man them fuss over

Tiger's bad outcome. Anancy and Dog did jus leave – jus go away about them business.

So Bro Nancy and Bro Dog dohn see the bandaged up Bro Tiger that the Tiger-man them take away, take away on horseback.

All the same, that day dohn change Tiger at all. It dohn stop Tiger from givin Anancy a bad challenge.

Inside the story

In pairs or groups

This is a typical Anancy story, in which the Spiderman overcomes the much stronger Tiger by means of a clever trick. Although it appears to be such a simple story, it is interesting to see just how Anancy persuades Tiger to take the final step into the concealed trap.

1 Anancy appears unarmed and with only one friend against Tiger's might. What effect does this have on Tiger?

2 Instead of shouting out defiantly, Anancy offers himself to Tiger saying, 'Come and chop off my head. Let the world know you are a brave-brave man.' Discuss why this makes Tiger feel he can't now attack Anancy.

3 Why does Tiger now want the whole world to know that he is 'good-good friends' with Anancy?

4 Anancy makes a point of saying, 'You invite yourself into my yard, I don't say go away. You want to shake my hand, I don't say oh no.' Who is Tiger to blame for what then happens?

Is the story as simple as it appears to be at first?

On your own

The titles of some of the other Anancy stories are intriguing: 'Anancy and Looking for a Wife'; 'Anancy, Old Witch and King-Daughter'; 'Tiger and the Stump-a-Foot Celebration Dance' – these are just three from James Berry's collection, *Anancy Spiderman*. Write your own Anancy story, maybe using one of these titles to give you an idea for a starting-point.

In small groups

1 The confrontation between Anancy and Tiger is stage-managed very successfully by Anancy who knows exactly what he wants to happen. You could turn the story into a play, starting at the point when Tiger arrives in all his glory. To begin with, you will have to think of some words to cover what has happened in the story so far. For example, Tiger might announce why he is there (Tiger's challenge and Anancy's Invitation to come and bring his friends) and wonder aloud at Anancy's daring to stand against him. Alternatively, you could use a Narrator to explain the situation.

2 A different way of dramatising the tale is to use a shadow puppet theatre. Shadow puppets require only simple figures cut from card and pressed against a backlit screen so that they appear silhouetted as shadows. Out of sight of the audience, you manipulate the figures and provide the characters' voices. The figures are mounted on light rods (pea-sticks will do) and scenery is also cut out and mounted in the same way. For this production you could manage with just the two main figures, Tiger and Anancy, but you might like to be more adventurous and add Tiger's horse and Anancy's friend, Dog, as well as assorted Tiger warriors carrying spears and axes. Don't forget you will need a concealed pit and perhaps a gate to Anancy's yard.

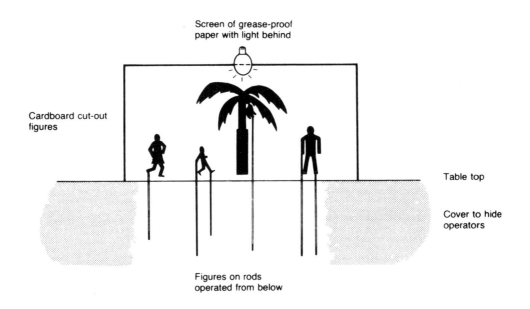

Screen of grease-proof paper with light behind

Cardboard cut-out figures

Table top

Cover to hide operators

Figures on rods operated from below

The following animal fable about the Tiger is a folk-tale from India. It is translated from a collection of tales known as the *Hitopadesha* which is the source of many similar stories that have found their way into western literature. As usual with such fables, it aims to teach us something about the way *people*, not animals, behave. As you read it, think about what you think the story is teaching us – what the *moral* is.

THE PRICE OF GREED

retold by J. E. B. Gray

Once upon a time in the southern forests there dwelt a certain old tiger. Every day he would take a ceremonial bath and, gathering some sacred *kusha* grass in his paw, he would call out to the passers-by as he sat at the edge of a pond: 'Ho there, good travellers, take this golden bracelet!' One day a certain traveller was attracted by greed on hearing the words of the tiger and he thought to himself: This is a lucky chance! But I must not be hasty where a risk is involved for, people say, the result of getting a desirable object from an undesirable source is not good; indeed, even nectar, when tainted with poison, brings about one's death. Still, the search after wealth is always attended by danger, and on this point I have heard it said that no man attains a fortune unless he embarks on an adventure. Then, if he risks everything and survives, he truly gains a fortune. Let me therefore look carefully into this matter. Thereupon he called aloud: 'Where is your bracelet?'

The tiger stretched out a paw and showed it to him, but the traveller said: 'How am I to trust someone with a murderous nature like yours?'

The tiger replied: 'Listen, worthy traveller. Long ago, in the days of my youth, I was most certainly very wicked and I killed many a cow and many a Brahman. As a result of my sins, my wife and my children died and now I am without heirs. One day then a saintly man advised me to practise charity and to lead a holy life. I followed his advice, so that I am now in the habit of taking ritual baths and giving presents. I am old now, and my claws and my teeth have fallen out; how then could you fail to have confidence in me? Indeed,' the tiger went on, 'I am so utterly free from all desires that I am willing to give away this golden bracelet which I hold in my paw to anyone who wants it. I admit it is difficult to overcome the belief that tigers eat people, but I, for my part, have studied the laws of religion. You are a poor fellow, and so I would like you to have this bracelet. A gift which is given for the sake of giving to one who can make no return is, they say, the very best of gifts, and especially if made at the proper time and place and to the proper person. Come and bathe in the pool then and accept the bracelet from me.'

The traveller felt confidence at the tiger's words, but no sooner did he enter the pool in order to bathe than he found himself stuck fast in the mud and unable to run away. When the tiger saw him held deep in the mud he said: 'Oho! you have fallen into the mud; I will just lift you out of it.'

With these words he gently approached the traveller.

As the traveller was seized by the tiger, he thought to himself: The fact that he studies the laws of religion is certainly no reason for having confidence in a villain; indeed, it is the nature of the person that counts, just as the milk of cows by nature is sweet. I did not do well in having faith in this murderous beast, for even the moon is swallowed by Rāhu, the demon of the eclipse. So fate ordains it, and who can wipe out the decrees of fate?

With these and other thoughts passing through his mind, the traveller was killed by the tiger and eaten.

Inside the story

In groups

1 Have you thought about the moral of the story? You could say that the story is warning us not to be tempted when tigers offer us valuable bracelets or we might be eaten up. But that's not something that happens very often! What more everyday warnings does the story give us?

2 There is an old saying that 'the leopard cannot change his spots and the tiger cannot change his stripes'. There is another old saying that 'The devil can cite Scripture for his purpose'. Talk about what you think these mean and how they may be related to this story.

3 Can you think of similar but more everyday situations in which people might be tempted and deceived by smooth talk, only to find themselves lured into a difficult position or even mortal danger?

4 This story is part of the oral tradition: that is, it was originally *told* rather than written down. Read it over again to get the main points of the tale clear in your mind and try to retell it – in a mixture of your own words and what sticks vividly in your mind from the original – to other members of the group, *without* looking at the text.

5 The tale could be dramatised as a small play or a mime with a Narrator telling the story, or it could be turned into a shadow puppet production, as outlined for the Anancy story on p. 43.

On your own

Tiger gets what he wants by sweet-talking and by pretending he has changed his ways. He also knows that human beings are easily tempted by riches. Write your own story on the same theme in which a cunning animal, perhaps a fox, a wolf or a leopard, deceives either a human being or another creature by using similar tricks. Of course, you need a different temptation from the bracelet of this story and a different trap from the muddy lake.

In this retelling of an old Irish tale, it is not the mighty hero but the hero's wife who uses superior intelligence to prevent a likely defeat. As such tales were often passed down from generation to generation by the women in the family (literally 'old wives' tales'), it is hardly surprising that many focus on the inventiveness and quickwittedness of women, and laugh at the absurdities and incompetence of men.

Two Giants

Edna O'Brien

Finn was the biggest and the bravest giant in all of Ireland. His deeds were known far and wide, lions lay down before him, his chariot flashed like a comet through the fields of battle, and with his 'Venomous' Sword he lay low a hundred men while with the other hand casting his sling at a troop of deer or a herd of wild boar. Along with that he had a thumb of knowledge and when he sucked this thumb he could tell what was happening anywhere in Ireland and he could foretell the future encounters. Now when Finn was no longer young, the rumour went about that there was a giant in Scotland who was Finn's equal and his name was McConigle. McConigle was not only fierce in battle, but when he walked up a hill the earth trembled under his feet, the trees wobbled, and the wild game fled to their lairs. By one blow of his fist he flattened a thunderbolt one day, turned it into the shape of a pancake and kept it in his pocket as a souvenir. He too had a way of prophesising by putting his middle finger into his mouth and sucking on it. Now the giants had never met but it was reported that McConigle intended to come over to Ireland, to fight Finn and to give him a pasting.

It so happened that one day Finn and his men were away from home and were busy making a bridge across the Giant's Causeway. In the distance they could see a messenger galloping towards them and Finn wondered if his wife Oonagh had taken sick or if there had been some breach in their fortifications at home. The messenger announced that Finn was to come home at once and then whispered something in Finn's ear that made him tremble with rage.

'So he's on my trail,' said Finn as he stood up and with that he pulled up a big fir tree, banged the clay off it and with his knife snedded it into a walking stick, so that it was both a walking stick and an umbrella. To see Finn walk was like seeing a mountain move and in no time he was across one county and heading towards home. He was going up a slope when in the mud he saw footmarks which were as big as his own. In fact they were the exact shape as his own and Finn thought, Lo, and had his first feeling of terror and doubt. Never before had he come across a giant the length and breadth of whose feet were as enormous as his own. He widened his chest and let out an almighty roar just to make his presence felt and it echoed all over the valley and was heard by his wife in her own home.

Finn's palace was on the top of a hill called Knockmany and it looked out on another mountain called Culamore and there was a deep gorge in between. Finn had settled there so that he could see his enemies a long way off and as well as that he could throw the bodies of his prey into the gorge for the crows to fatten themselves on.

'Oh my bilberry,' said Finn as he saw his wife Oonagh who had plaited her hair and put on a silk dress to please him. At once Finn asked if the reason she had sent for him was true.

'Tis true, Avick,' said Oonagh and went on to tell him how McConigle had pitched tent at the far side of the province and had his famous thunderbolt in the shape of a pancake in his pocket, and called himself The Invincible. Finn put his thumb into his mouth to verify all these things and found that they were true. He could only use his gift of prophecy on very trying and solemn occasions such as this was.

'Finn darling, don't bite your thumb,' said Oonagh very sweetly as she led him into the house where there was a dinner prepared. Finn squatted at one end of the low table, Oonagh at the other, and along with maidens to wait on them there were harpists playing in order to soothe Finn. He started by having sixteen duck eggs, eight pig's crubeens and three raw onions for his digestion. The main course was a haunch of roast venison and it was so long that it stretched between them down the length of the table, a sizzling roast dotted with berries and all sorts of herbs. But no matter how much he ate or drank there was a frown on Finn's forehead and a big brown ridge like a furrow on the bridge of his nose because of his thinking.

'Dearest,' said Oonagh as she bobbed along and began to stroke his great naked back. Finn always removed his cloak before he sat down to eat.

'You'll best him, you always do,' said Oonagh, but Finn shook his head and said it was perilous because according to his thumb he and McConigle had equal amounts of strength, ate the same amount of food, weighed the same, and were equally matched in daring, wisdom and cunning.

'What else does it say?' Oonagh asked and Finn put his thumb right inside his mouth and shut his eyes in order to concentrate.

'Take care you don't draw blood,' said Oonagh.

'He's coming,' said Finn, 'he's below in Dungannon,' and at that he jumped up.

'When will he be here?' said Oonagh.

'He'll be here before long,' said Finn and he began to put his vest and his jacket on. He looked at his wife and for the first time she saw fear and apprehension in his eyes. She decided that she would have to help him and make use of her own enchantments. Oonagh was in with the fairies too and with her wand had once turned a hussy into a hound. She told Finn that she would help him to succeed.

'How, how,' said Finn, hitting the table and sending delph* in all directions.

Oonagh hurried out of the doorway in order to give a message to her sister who lived on the opposite mountain at Culamore.

'Grania,' said Oonagh, 'are you at home?'

'I'm in the kitchen garden,' said Grania, 'I'm picking berries for a tart.'

'Run up to the top of the hill and look about you and tell us if you see anything untoward,' said Oonagh. They waited for a few minutes with Finn

*pots, pottery

pacing up and down and servants fanning him with great leaves.

'I am there now,' said Grania.

'What do you see?' said Oonagh.

'Oh lawsie me,' exclaimed Grania, 'I see the biggest giant I've ever seen coming out of the town of Dungannon.'

'What is he like?' said Oonagh.

'He's something terrible to behold,' said Grania and went on to describe a giant of about twelve feet in height, his hair all the way down to his waist, his face ruddy like any giant's except that he had daubed blood over it and, most unnerving of all, his three eyes. He had an eye in the middle of his head that was rolling round like the hands of a clock. Not only was the ground shaking beneath him but the birds in the trees were dying of fright. Along with that he was laughing out loud as if he had just heard the most hilarious joke.

'He's coming up to leather Finn,' said Oonagh to her sister.

'Finn has my sympathy,' said Grania and then she just announced that the giant had picked up a white goat and was wringing its neck and was obviously going to eat it raw.

'I'll tell you what,' said Oonagh, 'call down to him and invite him up to your place for a bite to eat.'

'Why so?' said Finn, unable to follow his wife's drift of thought.

'Strategy,' said Oonagh, 'strategy.'

Grania called across to say she'd be glad to oblige and she'd entertain the monster but she was a bit short of bacon and of butter.

'I'll fling you some across,' said Oonagh and she snapped her fingers for a servant to bring a flitch of bacon and a firkin of butter. However, before throwing them she forgot to say her charms and didn't the butter and the bacon fall into a stream and get carried away.

'Never mind,' said Grania, 'I'll give him heather soup and I'll put shredded bark in it to give him indigestion.'

'Good on you,' said Oonagh and she winked at Finn.

'He'll skewer me,' said Finn.

'Don't be ridiculous,' said Oonagh although to tell you the truth she could see a situation where she herself might be a dainty morsel, a little fritter for the giant's supper.

'My courage is leaving me, I'll be disgraced,' said Finn.

'Two heads are better than one,' said Oonagh as she went towards the place where she kept her magic threads. She drew nine woollen threads of different colours, she plaited them into three plaits, with three colours in each one; she put a plait on her right arm, another round her right ankle, a third round her heart, and in that way Oonagh was protected. Then she got going. She asked the servants to go up in the loft and bring down iron griddles and a child's cradle. She got them to make cakes but she hid the griddles inside the cakes and then baked them in the fire in the usual way. When they were done she dusted them over with flour so as to hide any protuberances and she put them in the window to cool. Then she put down a large pot of milk which she later made into curds and whey and showed Finn how to pick up a curd in his hand and make it smooth as a stone. Then she got a nightgown and a shawl and dressed Finn in it and put a nightcap on his head. She told him that he would have to get into the cradle and completely cover himself with clothes, with only his two eyes peering out.

'I can't fit in a cradle,' said Finn.

'You'll have to double up,' said Oonagh.

'I'll have to triple up,' said Finn as she pushed him towards it.

'You must pass for your own child,' said Oonagh.

'But I'm not a child,' said Finn and he was afraid that he had taken the cowardice too far. Oonagh ignored his mutterings and just put him into the cradle and covered him up with great wool blankets and red deerskins.

'What do I do?' said Finn.

'Whist,' said Oonagh because they could hear the bruiser coming up the hill and giving a skelp of his axe to the dogs to shut them up. He strutted across the courtyard and when he arrived at their door he put a hand around either oak pillar and bellowed:

'Anyone home?'

Oonagh came forward all shy and mincing and gave a little gasp to signify to him how formidable he was. He had rat skins and coon skins dangling from his ears and his third eye was rolling about like a spinning top.

'Mr McConigle,' said Oonagh.

'The great McConigle,' said the giant and then asked if he was in the house of Finn.

'Indeed you are,' said Oonagh and gestured towards a chair to make him welcome.

'You're Mrs Finn, I suppose,' said the giant.

'I am,' said she, 'and a proud wife at that.'

'Thinks he's the toughest giant in Ireland,' said McConigle.

'It's a proven fact,' said his wife proudly.

'There's a man within three feet of you that's very desirous of having a tussle with him,' said McConigle and he looked around in order to sniff out his rival.

'Is he hiding from me?' he asked.

'Hiding?' said Oonagh. 'He left here frothing, he's gone out to find you and it's lucky for you you didn't meet him, or you'd be a dead man now, your head on his pike as an ornament.'

'You vixen,' said McConigle and he roared with rage but Oonagh was in no way dismayed.

'He's twice your height and much better built,' said she.

'You don't know my strength,' said McConigle.

'In that case would you turn the house,' said Oonagh.

The giant stood up, put his middle finger in his mouth, thought for an instant, then went out, put his arms around the house, picked it up and put it facing a different way. Finn in his cradle was now facing in a different direction and there was sweat pouring out of him with heat and nerves.

'You're a handy giant,' said Oonagh and then told

him that she was short of water, but that there was a fine spring under some rocks and that if he could split the rocks she'd be most obliged. He took his axe out from under his leather apron, struck at the rocks and tore a cleft that was hundreds of feet deep. Oonagh began to have doubts.

'Come in and eat,' said she and added that although her husband would make mince of him, the laws of hospitality must be observed.

She placed before him six cakes of bread and a mound of newly churned butter and she sat down pretending to be polite. He put one of the cakes in his mouth, took a bite and let out the most terrible growl.

'What kind of bread is this?' he said fiercely.

'Fresh bread,' said Oonagh, cool as a breeze.

'And here are two teeth of mine gone,' said he as he hauled out two big molars that were grey in colour and shaped like drinking horns.

'Why,' said Oonagh, 'that's Finn's bread, the only bread that he eats, him and the child here.' At that she offered another cake. As soon as he put it in his mouth another great crack was heard and he let out a yell far fiercer than the first, so that the baby mewled. 'Thunder and giblets,' said he as he pulled out two more teeth with bits of gum on them.

'Well, Mr McConigle,' said Oonagh, 'if you can't manage the bread, don't bother with it but don't be disturbing my child.'

'Mammy, mammy, can I have some bread,' said the baby from the cradle and its voice gave McConigle a start. Oonagh very cleverly handed a cake that had no griddle in and McConigle was flabbergasted as he watched the child gobble it up.

'I'd like to take a glimpse at that lad in the cradle,' said he.

'Certainly,' said Oonagh and she told the little

baby to get up and prove himself the worthy child of his father. Now the baby stood up, looked at McConigle and said, 'Are you as strong as me?'

'Thundering giblets,' said McConigle, 'how dare you insult me.'

'Can you squeeze water out of a stone?' said the child, and he put a stone into McConigle's hand. McConigle squeezed and squeezed but not a drop of liquid came out.

'Watch me,' said the child and he put his hands under the covers, took out one of the white curds that looked exactly like a stone and squeezed until the liquid came out in a little shower from his hands.

'My daddy is training me,' said he, 'but I have a lot to learn yet.'

McConigle was speechless.

'I'll go back to sleep now,' said the child, 'but I'd hate to waste my time on anyone that hasn't my daddy's strength, that can't eat daddy's bread or squeeze water out of a stone.' Then he slipped down and as Oonagh was pulling the covers up over him he raised his index finger and gave a word of warning to McConigle. 'I'd be off out of here if I were you as it's in flummery my father will have you.'

'What he says is a fact,' said Oonagh as she tucked Finn into the cradle and patted him to let him know how proud she was.

'I'm thinking it is,' said McConigle.

'You're not in his league at all,' said Oonagh and went on to remind McConigle that if the child was that strong he could only guess at the immensity of the father.

'Will you let me feel the teeth of that infant?' said he still in a quandry.

'By all means,' said Oonagh and she took his hand and she stuck it straight into Finn's mouth explaining that the child's best teeth were in the back of his head. McConigle was amazed to find a baby with a full set of grinders and more amazed when he felt something snap and then felt his finger detach itself and when he pulled out his hand there was a big wound where his finger of knowledge had been. Finn had eaten it. So shocked was he and so horror-stricken that he fell down. Finn rose from the cradle and laid roundly on the monster with his bare hands. He could easily have killed him with his sword but that McConigle begged for his life and Finn being a chivalrous hero gave it to him. After that McConigle made his peace, picked up his teeth and his accoutrements and promised to go home to Scotland and never set foot in Ireland again.

Inside the story

Tales like this one about Finn, and the next one about 'The Wise Little Girl', are very old and belong to the folk – that is, the ordinary people, the peasantry. It is they, and particularly the women, who have kept many such tales alive, passing them on to their children.

In pairs

1 What sort of character is Finn? Look through the story and see what evidence you can find to support your view of him.

2 What sort of character is Oonagh? Again, look through the text and collect any evidence to support your view of her.

On your own

1 Produce a strip-cartoon version of the story for a younger class. Use speech bubbles inside the frames of your drawings and a small amount of text underneath each illustration.

2 There are several descriptions of what the Scottish giant McConigle looks like and how he behaves. He's twelve feet tall, hairy, daubed with blood and has three eyes. We know quite a bit about Finn, the Irish giant, too. Invent your own English or Welsh giant, or perhaps a giant from another country, and write a detailed description of him or her. Don't concentrate simply on physical description: remember to mention how your giant is dressed, what he or she eats, how he or she speaks, what his or her character is like, and so on. When you have finished, you might like to illustrate the character you have invented.

3 Now that you have invented your own giant, write a story for younger children about a contest between your giant and either Finn or McConigle. You may find it helpful to think of another situation which calls for a trick.

Angela Carter, who retells this old Russian folk-tale, says that the story is 'a battle of wits in three rounds'. A young child takes on a powerful adult – no less a person than the tsar, the Emperor of Russia himself. The story appears in several versions in different countries, including Czechoslovakia and Scandinavia, and has probably been in existence for several hundred years. An ancient carving in the old Coventry cathedral showed a character similar to the girl in this story – 'a long-haired woman wrapped in a net, riding sideways on a goat and preceded by a hare.' The tale may have connections with pagan, magical beliefs.

It is one of many stories in which the main character is put in a seemingly impossible situation and has to carry out some formidable task or solve a daunting riddle. In some stories the person setting the task is sure that it cannot be done. Whatever the circumstances, the resourceful hero or heroine manages to turn the tables.

THE WISE LITTLE GIRL

Angela Carter

Two brothers were traveling together: one was poor and the other was rich, and each had a horse, the poor one a mare, and the rich one a gelding. They stopped for the night, one beside the other. The poor man's mare bore a foal during the night, and the foal rolled under the rich man's cart. In the morning the rich man roused his poor brother, saying: 'Get up, brother. During the night my cart bore a foal.' The brother rose and said: 'How is it possible for a cart to give birth to a foal? It was my mare who bore the foal!' The rich brother said: 'If your mare were his mother, he would have been found lying beside her.' To settle their quarrel they went to the authorities. The rich man gave the judges money and the poor man presented his case in words.

Finally word of this affair reached the tsar himself. He summoned both brothers before him and proposed to them four riddles: 'What is the strongest and swiftest thing in the world? What is the fattest thing in the world? What is the softest thing? And what is the loveliest thing?' He gave them three days' time and said: 'On the fourth day come back with your answers.'

The rich man thought and thought, remembered his god-mother, and went to ask her advice. She bade him sit down to table, treated him to food and drink, and then asked: 'Why are you so sad, my godson?' 'The sovereign has proposed four riddles to me, and given me only three days to solve them.' 'What are the riddles? Tell me.' 'Well, godmother, this is the first riddle: "What is the strongest and swiftest thing in the world?"' 'That's not difficult! My husband has a bay mare; nothing in the world is swifter than she is; if you lash her with a whip she will overtake a hare.' 'The second riddle is: "What is the fattest thing in the world?"' 'We have been feeding a spotted boar for the last two years; he has become so fat that he can barely stand on his legs.' 'The third riddle is: "What is the softest thing in the world?"' 'That's well known. Eider down – you cannot think of anything softer.' 'The fourth riddle is: "What is the loveliest thing in the world?"' 'The loveliest thing in the world is my grandson Ivanushka.' 'Thank you, godmother, you have advised me well. I shall be grateful to you for the rest of my life.'

As for the poor brother, he shed bitter tears and went home. He was met by his seven-year-old daughter – she was his only child – who said: 'Why are you sighing and shedding tears, Father?' 'How can I help sighing and shedding tears? The tsar has proposed four riddles to me, and I shall never be able to solve them.' 'Tell me, what are these riddles?' 'Here they are, my little daughter: "What is the strongest and swiftest thing in the world? What is the fattest thing, what is the softest thing, and what is the loveliest thing?"' 'Father, go to the tsar and tell him that the strongest and fastest thing in the world is the wind; the fattest is the earth, for she feeds everything that grows and lives; the softest of all is the hand, for whatever a man may lie on, he puts his hand under his head; and there is nothing lovelier in the world than sleep.'

The two brothers, the poor one and the rich one, came to the tsar. The tsar heard their answers to the riddles, and asked the poor man: 'Did you solve these riddles yourself, or did someone solve them for you?' The poor man answered: 'Your Majesty, I have a seven-year-old daughter, and she gave me the answers.' 'If your daughter is so wise, here is a silken thread for her; let her weave an embroidered towel for me by tomorrow morning.' The peasant took the silken thread and came home sad and grieving. 'We are in trouble,' he said to his daughter. 'The tsar has ordered you to weave a towel from this thread.' 'Grieve not, Father,' said the little girl. She broke off a twig from a broom, gave it to her father, and told him: 'Go to the tsar and ask him to find a master

who can make a loom from this twig; on it I will weave his towel.' The peasant did as his daughter told him. The tsar listened to him and gave him a hundred and fifty eggs, saying: 'Give these eggs to your daughter; let her hatch one hundred and fifty chicks by tomorrow.'

The peasant returned home, even more sad and grieving than the first time. 'Ah, my daughter,' he said, 'you are barely out of one trouble before another is upon you.' 'Grieve not, Father,' answered the seven-year-old girl. She baked the eggs for dinner and for supper and sent her father to the king. 'Tell him,' she said to her father, 'that one-day grain is needed to feed the chicks. In one day let a field be plowed and the millet sown, harvested, and threshed; our chickens refuse to peck any other grain.' The tsar listened to this and said: 'Since your daughter is so wise, let her appear before me tomorrow morning – and I want her to come neither on foot nor on horseback, neither naked nor dressed, neither with a present nor without a gift.' 'Now,' thought the peasant, 'even my daughter cannot solve such a difficult riddle; we are lost.' 'Grieve not,' his seven-year-old daughter said to him. 'Go to the hunters and buy me a live hare and a live quail.' The father bought her a hare and a quail.

Next morning the seven-year-old girl took off her clothes, donned a net, took the quail in her hand, sat upon the hare, and went to the palace. The tsar met her at the gate. She bowed to him, saying, 'Here is a little gift for you, Your Majesty,' and handed him the quail. The tsar stretched out his hand, but the quail shook her wings and – flap, flap! – was gone. 'Very well,' said the tsar, 'you have done as I ordered you to do. Now tell me – since your father is so poor, what do you live on?' 'My father catches fish on the shore, and he never puts bait in the water; and I make fish soup in my skirt.' 'You are stupid! Fish never live on the shore, fish live in the water.' 'And you – are you wise? Who ever saw a cart bear foals? Not a cart but a mare bears foals.'

The tsar awarded the foal to the poor peasant and took the daughter into his own palace; when she grew up he married her and she became the tsarina.

Inside the story

In groups

1 What is the difference between the rich and the poor brother's behaviour when they go to the judges?

2 How are the answers each gives to the riddles different?

3 Discuss why you think the tsar preferred the poor man's answers.

4 Why do you think the tsar was willing to enter into a battle of wits with the little girl?

5 What pleases him about the way she makes her replies?

6 Riddling stories are very common and you can probably find other examples in books in your school or local library.

You may know the riddles that Gollum and Bilbo swap in Tolkien's story, *The Hobbit*, or you may know that oldest of all riddles – the Riddle of the Sphinx which was solved by Oedipus; or the story of 'The Clever Little Tailor' by the brothers Grimm; or the story of the Princess *Turandot* who can only be won by the man who correctly guesses the answer to three riddles. In Shakespeare's play, *The Merchant of Venice*, the hand of Portia can be won only by the man who correctly guesses in which one of three caskets – of gold, silver and lead – her portrait is hidden. Such riddles are not often like the riddles modern nine year olds tell each other (for example, *Q. What grows longer the more you take away from it? A. a ditch*), but are more often like the examples in the story you have just read.

Sometimes the task set in a story is not to answer a riddle but rather to undertake what seems to be something impossible. In the story of 'Rumpelstiltskin' (sometimes called

'Tom-tit-Tot') a girl has to spin straw and also to guess Rumpelstiltskin's name.

See if you can track down one or two examples of riddle stories and 'impossible task' stories.

To do this, first share with the rest of your group any memories you have of such stories. (You may recall some from television or film rather than from books.) Do you, for example, know any of the tales mentioned above? Next, ask your teacher and librarian where you can find these and other riddling stories. Look up the names in the library catalogue. If the riddle is only a small part of a much longer story, as in *The Merchant of Venice* or *The Hobbit*, just concentrate on the riddle part. Share your findings with the class. You might be able to prepare a wall display of different riddle and task stories together with some of your own illustrations.

On your own

Write your own riddling or 'impossible task' story. First you will need to think about **what the prize is and who wants it**. (In the traditional story, the prize was often the hand of the princess in marriage, but these days that may not be so appropriate.) Gollum and Bilbo riddled for possession of the Ring of Power in *The Hobbit*; dragons might be persuaded to riddle for possession of their treasure hoards; Batman has had to riddle for his very life against the evil Riddler . . . but the prize could be something as ordinary as winning at hockey or football, or the cancellation of the maths test tomorrow. Next, you have to think about **who sets the riddle or task**. It has to be somebody capable of delivering the magical prize so it is probably going to be some kind of magical person or creature – a strange demon who appears unannounced, perhaps; a pet cat that turns out to have magical powers; the old man or woman who always sits on the same park bench when you go shopping . . . Then you have to think **what the riddle or task should be**. And from there onwards the story should begin to unfold.

Ray Bradbury's story of 'The Invisible Boy' offers us two tricksters. One is a lonely old lady who devises a clever way of keeping a boy with her for company; the other is the boy himself who feels that he can play all kinds of tricks on the old lady. Just who is tricking whom is an interesting question you might ask yourself as the story unfolds.

THE INVISIBLE BOY

Ray Bradbury

She took the great iron spoon and the mummified frog and gave it a bash and made dust of it, and talked to the dust while she ground it in her stony fists quickly. Her beady gray bird-eyes flickered at the cabin. Each time she looked, a head in the small thin window ducked as if she'd fired off a shotgun.

'Charlie!' cried Old Lady. 'You come outa there! I'm fixing a lizard magic to unlock that rusty door! You come out now and I won't make the earth shake or the trees go up in fire or the sun set at high noon!'

The only sound was the warm mountain light on the high turpentine trees, a tufted squirrel chittering around and around on a green-furred log, the ants moving in a fine brown line at Old Lady's bare, blue-veined feet.

'You been starving in there two days, darn you!' she panted, chiming the spoon against a flat rock, causing the plump gray miracle bag to swing at her waist. Sweating sour, she rose and marched at the cabin, bearing the pulverized flesh. 'Come out, now!' She flicked a pinch of power inside the lock. 'All right, I'll come get you!' she wheezed.

She spun the knob with one walnut-colored hand, first one way, then the other. 'O Lord,' she intoned, 'fling this door wide!'

When nothing flung, she added yet another philtre and held her breath. Her long untidy skirt rustled as she peered into her bag of darkness to see if she had any scaly monsters there, any charm finer than the frog she'd killed months ago for such a crisis as this.

She heard Charlie breathing against the door. His folks had pranced off into some Ozark town early this week, leaving him, and he'd run almost six miles to Old Lady for company – she was by way of being an aunt or cousin or some such, and he didn't mind her fashions.

But then, two days ago, Old Lady, having gotten used to the boy around, decided to keep him for convenient company. She pricked her thin shoulder bone, drew out three blood pearls, spat wet over her right elbow, tromped on a crunch-cricket, and at the same instant clawed her left hand at Charlie, crying, 'My son you are, you are my son, for all eternity!'

Charlie, bounding like a startled hare, had crashed off into the bush, heading for home.

But Old Lady, skittering quick as a gingham lizard, cornered him in a dead end, and Charlie holed up in this old hermit's cabin and wouldn't come out, no matter how she whammed door, window, or knothole with amber-colored fist or trounced her ritual fires, explaining to him that he was certainly her son *now*, all right.

'Charlie, you *there?*' she asked, cutting holes in the door planks with her bright little slippery eyes.

'I'm all of me here,' he replied finally, very tired.

Maybe he would fall out on the ground any moment. She wrestled the knob hopefully. Perhaps a pinch too much frog powder had grated the lock wrong. She always overdid or underdid her miracles, she mused angrily, never doing them just *exact*, Devil take it!

'Charlie, I only wants someone to night-prattle to, someone to warm hands with at the fire. Someone to fetch kindling for me mornings, and fight off the spunks that come creeping of early fogs! I ain't got no fetching on you for myself, son, just for your company.' She smacked her lips. 'Tell you what, Charles, you come out and *I teach* you things!'

'What things?' he suspicioned.

'Teach you how to buy cheap, sell high. Catch a snow weasel, cut off its head, carry it warm in your hind pocket. There!'

'Aw,' said Charlie.

She made haste. 'Teach you to make yourself shotproof. So if anyone bangs at you with a gun, nothing happens.'

When Charlie stayed silent, she gave him the secret in a high fluttering whisper. 'Dig and stitch mouse-ear roots on Friday during full moon, and wear 'em around your neck in a white silk.'

'You're crazy,' Charlie said.

'Teach you how to stop blood or make animals stand frozen or make blind horses see, all them things I'll teach you! Teach you to cure a swelled-up cow and unbewitch a goat. Show you how to make yourself invisible!'

'Oh,' said Charlie.

Old Lady's heart beat like a Salvation tambourine. The knob turned from the other side.

'You,' said Charlie, 'are funning me.'

'No, I'm not,' exclaimed Old Lady. 'Oh, Charlie, why, I'll make you like a window, see right through you. Why, child, you'll be surprised!'

'Real invisible?'

'Real invisible!'

'You won't fetch on to me if I walk out?'

'Won't touch a bristle of you, son.'

'Well,' he drawled reluctantly, 'all right.'

The door opened. Charlie stood in his bare feet, head down, chin against chest. 'Make me invisible,' he said.

'First we got to catch us a bat,' said Old Lady. 'Start lookin'!'

She gave him some jerky beef for his hunger and watched him climb a tree. He went high up and high up and it was nice seeing him there and it was nice having him here and all about after so many years alone with nothing to say good morning to but bird-droppings and silvery snail tracks.

Pretty soon a bat with a broken wing fluttered down out of the tree. Old Lady snatched it up, beating warm and shrieking between its porcelain white teeth, and Charlie dropped down after it, hand upon clenched hand, yelling.

That night, with the moon nibbling at the spiced pine cones, Old Lady extracted a long silver needle from under her wide blue dress. Gumming her excitement and secret anticipation, she sighted up the dead bat and held the cold needle steady-steady.

She had long ago realised that her miracles, despite all perspirations and salts and sulphurs, failed. But she had always dreamt that one day the miracles might start functioning, might spring up in crimson flowers and silver stars to prove that God had forgiven her for her pink body and her pink thoughts and her warm body and her warm thoughts as a young miss. But so far God had made no sign and said no word, but nobody knew this except Old Lady.

'Ready?' she asked Charlie, who crouched cross-kneed, wrapping his pretty legs in long goose-pimpled arms, his mouth open, making teeth. 'Ready,' he whispered, shivering.

'There!' She plunged the needle deep in the bat's right eye. 'So!'

'Oh!' screamed Charlie, wadding up his face.

'Now I wrap it in gingham, and here, put it in your pocket, keep it there, bat and all. Go on!'

He pocketed the charm.

'Charlie!' she shrieked fearfully. 'Charlie, where are you? I can't see you, child!'

'Here!' He jumped so the light ran in red streaks up his body. 'I'm here, Old Lady!' He stared wildly at his arms, legs, chest and toes. 'I'm here!'

Her eyes looked as if they were watching a thousand fireflies crisscrossing each other in the wild night air.

'Charlie, oh, you went fast! Quick as a hummingbird! Oh, Charlie, come back to me!'

'But I'm here!' he wailed.

'Where?'

'By the fire, the fire! And – and I can see myself. I'm not invisible at all!'

Old Lady rocked on her lean flanks. 'Course you can see you! Every invisible person knows himself. Otherwise, how could you eat, walk, or get around places? Charlie, touch me. Touch me so I know you.'

Uneasily he put out a hand.

She pretended to jerk, startled, at his touch. 'Ah!'

'You mean to say you can't find me?' he asked. 'Truly?'

'Not the least half rump of you!'

She found a tree to stare at, and stared at it with shining eyes, careful not to glance at him. 'Why, I sure did a trick that time!' She sighed with wonder. 'Whooeee. Quickest invisible I ever made! Charlie. Charlie, how you feel?'

'Like creek water – all stirred.'

'You'll settle.'

Then after a pause she added, 'Well, what you going to do now, Charlie, since you're invisible?'

All sorts of things shot through his brain, she could tell. Adventures stood up and danced like hell-fire in his eyes, and his mouth, just hanging, told what it meant to be a boy who imagined himself like the mountain winds. In a cold dream he said, 'I'll run across wheat fields, climb snow mountains, steal white chickens off'n farms. I'll kick pink pigs when they ain't looking. I'll pinch pretty girls' legs when they sleep, snap their garters in schoolrooms.' Charlie looked at Old Lady, and from the shiny tips of her eyes she saw something wicked shape his face. 'And other things I'll do, I'll do, I will,' he said.

'Don't try nothing on me,' warned Old Lady. 'I'm brittle as spring ice and I don't take handling.' Then: 'What about your folks?'

'My folks?'

'You can't fetch yourself home looking like that. Scare the inside ribbons out of them. Your mother'd faint straight back like timber falling. Think they want you about the house to stumble over and your ma have to call you every three minutes, even though you're in the room next her elbow?'

Charlie had not considered it. He sort of simmered down and whispered out a little 'Gosh' and felt of his long bones carefully.

'You'll be mighty lonesome. People looking through you like a water glass, people knocking you aside because they didn't reckon you to be underfoot. And women, Charlie, *women* –'

He swallowed. 'What about women?'

'No woman will be giving you a second stare. And no woman wants to be kissed by a boy's mouth they can't even *find*!'

Charlie dug his bare toe in the soil contemplatively. He pouted. 'Well, I'll stay invisible, anyway, for a spell. I'll have me some fun. I'll just be pretty careful, is all. I'll stay out from in front of wagons and horses and Pa. Pa shoots at the nariest sound.' Charlie blinked. 'Why, with me invisible, someday Pa might just up and fill me with buckshot, thinkin' I was a hill squirrel in the doorway. Oh . . .'

Old Lady nodded at a tree. 'That's likely.'

'Well,' he decided slowly, 'I'll stay invisible for to-night, and to-morrow you can fix me back all whole again, Old Lady.'

'Now if that ain't just like a critter, always wanting to be what he can't be,' remarked Old Lady to a beetle on a log.

'What you mean?' said Charlie.

'Why,' she explained, 'it was real hard work, fixing you up. It'll take a little *time* for it to wear off. Like a coat of paint wears off, boy.'

'You!' he cried. 'You did this to me! Now you make me back, you make me seeable!'

'Hush,' she said. 'It'll wear off, a hand or a foot at a time.'

'How'll it look, me around the hills with just one hand showing!'

'Like a five-winged bird hopping on the stones and bramble.'

'Or a foot showing!'

'Like a small pink rabbit jumping thicket.'

'Or my head floating!'

'Like a hairy balloon at the carnival!'

'How long before I'm *whole*?' he asked.

She deliberated that it might pretty well be an entire year.

He groaned. He began to sob and bite his lips and make fists. 'You magicked me, you did this, you did this thing to me. Now I won't be able to run home!'

She winked. 'But you *can* stay here, child, stay on with me real comfort-like, and I'll keep you fat and saucy.'

He flung it out: 'You did this on purpose! You mean old hag, you want to keep me here!'

He ran off through the shrubs on the instant.

'Charlie, come back!'

No answer but the pattern of his feet on the soft dark turf, and his wet choking cry which passed swiftly off and away.

She waited and then kindled herself a fire. 'He'll be back,' she whispered. And thinking inward on herself, she said, 'And now I'll have me my company through spring and into late summer. Then, when I'm tired of him and want a silence, I'll send him home.'

Charlie returned noiselessly with the first gray of dawn, gliding over the rimed turf to where Old Lady sprawled like a bleached stick before the scattered ashes.

He sat on some creek pebbles and stared at her.

She didn't dare look at him or beyond. He had made no sound, so how could she know he was anywhere about? She couldn't.

He sat there, tear marks on his cheeks.

Pretending to be just waking – but she had found no sleep from one end of the night to the other – Old Lady stood up, grunting and yawning, and turned in a circle to the dawn.

'Charlie?'

Her eyes passed from pines to soil, to sky, to the far hills. She called out his name, over and over again, and she felt like staring plumb straight at him, but she stopped herself. 'Charlie? Oh, Charles!' she called, and heard the echoes say the very same.

He sat, beginning to grin a bit, suddenly, knowing he was close to her, yet she must feel alone. Perhaps he felt the growing of a secret power, perhaps he felt secure from the world, certainly he was *pleased* with his invisibility.

She said aloud, 'Now where *can* that boy be? If he only made a noise so I could tell just where he is, maybe I'd fry him a breakfast.'

She prepared the morning victuals, irritated at his continuous quiet. She sizzled bacon on a hickory stick. 'The smell of it will draw his nose,' she muttered.

While her back was turned he swiped all the frying bacon and devoured it tastily.

She whirled, crying out, 'Lord!'

She eyed the clearing suspiciously. 'Charlie, that *you*?'

Charlie wiped his mouth clean on his wrists.

She trotted about the clearing, making like she was trying to locate him. Finally, with a clever thought, acting blind, she headed straight for him, groping. 'Charlie, where *are* you?'

A lightning streak, he evaded her, bobbing, ducking.

It took all her will power not to give chase; but you can't chase invisible boys, so she sat down, scowling, sputtering, and tried to fry more bacon. But every fresh strip she cut he would steal bubbling off the fire and run away far. Finally, cheeks burning, she cried, 'I know where you are! Right *there*! I hear you

run!' She pointed to one side of him, not too accurate. He ran again. 'Now you're there!' she shouted. 'There, and there!' pointing to all the places he was in the next five minutes. 'I hear you press a grass blade, knock a flower, snap a twig. I got fine shell ears, delicate as roses. They can hear the stars moving!'

Silently he galloped off among the pines, his voice trailing back, 'Can't hear me when I'm set on a rock. I'll just *set*!'

All day he sat on an observatory rock in the clear wind, motionless and sucking his tongue.

Old Lady gathered wood in the deep forest, feeling his eyes weaseling on her spine. She wanted to babble: 'Oh, I see you, I see you! I was only fooling about invisible boys! You're right there!' But she swallowed her gall and gummed it tight.

The following morning he did the spiteful things. He began leaping from behind trees. He made toad-faces, frog-faces, spider-faces at her, clenching down his lips with his fingers, popping his raw eyes, pushing up his nostrils so you could peer in and see his brain thinking.

Once she dropped her kindling. She pretended it was a blue jay startled her.

He made a motion as if to strangle her.

She trembled a little.

He made another move as if to bang her shins and spit on her cheek.

These motions she bore without a lid-flicker or a mouth-twitch.

He stuck out his tongue, making strange bad noises. He wiggled his loose ears so she wanted to laugh, and finally she did laugh and explained it away quickly by saying, 'Sat on a salamander! Whew, how it poked!'

By high noon the whole madness boiled to a

terrible peak.

For it was at that exact hour that Charlie came racing down the valley stark boy-naked!

Old Lady nearly fell flat with shock!

'Charlie!" she almost cried.

'Charlie raced naked up one side of a hill and naked down the other – naked as day, naked as the moon, raw as the sun and a newborn chick, his feet shimmering and rushing like the wings of a low-skimming hummingbird.

Old Lady's tongue locked in her mouth. What could she say? Charlie, go dress? For *shame*? *Stop* that? *Could* she? Oh, Charlie, Charlie, God! Could she say that now? *Well*?

Upon the big rock, she witnessed him dancing up and down, naked as the day of his birth, stomping bare feet, smacking his hands on his knees and sucking in and out his white stomach like blowing and deflating a circus balloon.

She shut her eyes tight and prayed.

After three hours of this she pleaded, 'Charlie, Charlie, come here! I got something to *tell* you!'

Like a fallen leaf he came, dressed again, praise the Lord.

'Charlie,' she said, looking at the pine trees, 'I see your right toe. *There* it is.'

'You do?' he said.

'Yes,' she said very sadly. 'There it is like a horny toad on the grass. And there, up there's your left ear hanging on the air like a pink butterfly.'

Charlie danced. 'I'm forming in, I'm forming in!'

Old Lady nodded. 'Here comes your ankle!'

'Gimme *both* my feet!' ordered Charlie.

'You got 'em.'

'How about my hands?'

'I see one crawling on your knee like a daddy longlegs.'

'How about the other one?'

'It's crawling too.'

'I got a body?'

'Shaping up fine.'

'I'll need my head to go home, Old Lady.'

To go home, she thought wearily. 'No!' she said, stubborn and angry. 'No, you ain't got no head. No head at all,' she cried. She'd leave that to the very last. 'No head, no head,' she insisted.

'No head?' he wailed.

'Yes, oh my God, yes, yes, you got your blamed head!' she snapped, giving up. 'Now, fetch me back my bat with the needle in his eye!'

He flung it at her. 'Haaaa-yoooo!' His yelling went all up the valley, and long after he had run toward home she heard his echoes, racing.

Then she plucked up her kindling with a great dry weariness and started back toward her shack, sighing, talking. And Charlie followed her all the way, *really* invisible now, so she couldn't see him, just hear him, like a pine cone dropping or a deep underground stream trickling, or a squirrel clambering a bough; and over the fire at twilight she and Charlie sat, him so invisible, and her feeding him bacon he wouldn't take, so she ate it herself, and then she fixed some magic and fell asleep with Charlie, made out of sticks and rags and pebbles, but still warm and her very own son, slumbering and nice in her shaking mother arms . . . and they talked about golden things in drowsy voices until dawn made the fire slowly, slowly wither out. . . .

Inside the story

In pairs or groups

1 It's a strange story. Think about which parts of it remain most vividly in your mind and why they made an impression. Find out whether others would choose the same parts of the story.

2 Does Old Lady really have magical powers? Does she believe that she has?

3 Discuss why you think she wants to keep the boy with her. Find quotations from the text that support your ideas.

4 How does Old Lady manage to keep up the pretence that Charlie is really invisible?

5 Do you think Charlie really believes himself to be invisible? Why does he behave as he does?

6 Talk about what you think happens in the long final sentence of the story and the feelings it leaves you with.

On your own

1 Charlie imagines all sorts of possibilities in being invisible and we see some of the mischief he gets up to, like stealing the bacon and pulling faces. Think of another trick he might well have played on Old Lady and how she might have responded. Write the scene in the same style as the original. That means looking closely at the way Ray Bradbury writes and finding the right 'voice' for Old Lady. It might help to imagine that your piece has to be inserted into the story so that anyone reading it for the first time can't tell what you have written and what is Bradbury's original.

2 Invisible boy, invisible girl – the mushrooms on toast you ate for breakfast have turned you invisible for a day. What happens?

In pairs

Act out some of the encounters between Old Lady and Charlie. The face pulling and bacon stealing incidents have lots of possibilities, as does the scene where Charlie gradually reappears. They can be mimed, but the words are full of life and it's worth learning some of them. Remember that in the first two encounters Old Lady has to avoid letting Charlie know she can see him and that Charlie feels free to be as naughty as he likes.

2
STRANGE TO TELL

As the title suggests, all the stories in this section are strange in some way and deal with things that are quite out of the ordinary. They all have an element of the supernatural. Not only are they *strange*, they are, above all, stories to *tell*, for as you read each one, you can hear the voice of the storyteller. Somehow they seem to insist that we should not simply read them to ourselves, but that we should at least read them aloud or, best of all, take them 'off' the page and *tell* them.

The first two stories, 'John Pettigrew's Mirror' and 'Lutey and the Mermaid', both come from Cornwall. The far west of England, with its many fishing villages in tiny sheltering bays set at the foot of high cliffs, facing often mountainous seas, is fertile ground for stories. The ever-changing sea dominates the lives of the people of Cornwall even today and was even more important in the past. To a fishing village, it was the great life-giver; it was also the great life-taker. But maybe nothing is ever wholly lost in the sea; things and people can undergo a 'sea change'. The poet e.e. cummings remarks:

> *For whatever we lose (like a you or a me)*
> *It's always ourselves we find in the sea*

Both these stories are, in many ways, about people finding themselves. But to do that, they have first to lose themselves in the tale. Listen to these stories read or told aloud. Lose yourself in the story – you never know what you may find!

JOHN PETTIGREW'S MIRROR
Ruth Manning-Sanders

This is a story my grandmother told me; nobody need believe it unless they wish, but everybody may believe it who will.

Well then, long ago there lived in a small seaside town an honest basket-maker, called John Pettigrew. He lived alone, for he had neither wife nor child, only an old shrew of a married cousin, Sarah Polgraine, who came in to cook and clean for him. John was as accustomed to Sarah's grumblings and scoldings as he was to the voice of the sea, and he did not notice them unless he was obliged to. He was grateful to her for looking after him, being thoroughly good-natured himself, and inclined to think well of his fellows, he had a conviction that, underneath all, Sarah was a good sort.

Underneath all, *everyone* was a good sort, so it seemed to John; but, when he tried to tell Sarah this, she would sniff and say, 'That's all *you* know!' And then she would point out everyone's faults and failings, and tell John to 'just look' at this, that, and the other one of their acquaintance! And John would shake his head, and say, 'That's a squint-eyed way of looking, cousin Sarah!' And Sarah would sniff again, and say *her* eyes saw plainly enough, and if some old fools would learn to face facts it would be more satisfactory for all concerned. But then John would chuckle, 'You're better than your words, Sarah, *I* know!' And with that he would leave her, and go out to the yard where he worked, and where the sound of her scolding voice reached him but faintly.

This yard of John's was built against the sea wall; there was a shed in it for wet weather, and plenty of sunshine when the skies were clear; and there he would spend his days, among the ozier bundles and the big and little baskets, that were some of them severely practical, and some cunningly decorated, according to his mood and fancy. A leisurely yet useful life was John's, with plenty of time for contemplation, and for an occasional tune on his mouth-organ when his fingers grew tired, or his mind felt the need of refreshment.

One stormy afternoon in late summer, John took a sack and went down to the sea shore in search of wreck-wood. The shore was littered with shining brown ribbons of seaweed, and the wood that he gathered was all tangled up with sand and shells. Great waves staggered and broke along the shore, and the run of them swirled up around John's feet, so that sometimes he was ankle-deep, and sometimes high and dry. From the tops of the breakers an off-sea wind flung foam into his eyes. The low and watery sun, shooting its rays from amidst rapidly moving storm clouds, brightened the foam, and flung wide mirrors of light across the backs and amongst the hollows of the mountainous waves that rose and fell beyond the breakers. And in these waves two seals, an old one and a young one, were merrily playing. Up they floated like things of cork, and down they dived swift as birds flying; and when they dived John saw the shadow of their bodies through the waves, and when they floated up he saw their big eyes shining.

'Blessed creatures!' thought John. 'No need to ask if you are happy!' And they do say that all the wisdom of the deep unsearchable flows through your oily noddles!'

A powerful gust of wind set him stumbling backwards. The sun vanished in the gathering storm; between two close-packed clouds a wan fork of lightning flashed through the grey air; thunder rolled echoing among the rocks; a deluge of rain dropped its murky curtains between John and all else; and through this curtain came the roar of the unsearchable deep where the seals played.

'Time this old man was safe indoors!' thought John. And he slung his sack over his shoulder and made for home.

What a night to be sure! In all his long life John could not remember such another one. The wind boomed in the chimney, and the smoke blew down it; the light in the lamp jumped and flared and sooted the lamp-glass. The windows shook and clattered as the rain lashed them. The wind flung itself against the door like a wild beast determined to get in; and, at every thud the door gave, all the crocks on the dresser set up a protesting rattle. From every crack and hole came shrieks, whistles, hootings, flutings and trumpetings; and behind all sounded the steady roar of the sea, crazed and billowing, dementedly leaping the wall beyond John's yard, and washing in among his ozier bundles and piles of baskets – even volleying under the kitchen door in a series of mad chuckles and lunatic snickerings, that added their small frenzy to the general hubbub.

John set a sandbag against the door, and hung up a blower in front of the fire. The storm seized the house in its fists and shook it, like a man rattling a dice-box.

'But the house is builded upon a rock,' thought John; and, offering up a prayer for those 'that do business in deep waters', he put on his spectacles and took down his Bible.

'They mount up to the heaven, they go down again to the deeps . . . They reel to and fro, and stagger like a drunken man, and are at their wits' end. Then they cry . . .'

Bang! Crash! A wave hit the kitchen door with the roar of a cannon. And – heark'ee! – out there, a strange cry, that was neither bleat, nor bark, nor the groan of a man. One cry, and then no more. 'If 'twere a fiend from hell,' thought John, 'on such a night a man must ope his door to 't.' And, laying his spectacles between the leaves of his Bible, he kicked the sandbag aside, and pulled back the door.

The wind came into the kitchen with a whoop and a gallop; the lamp flared and went out; the fire roared, and the blower clattered on to the hearthstone. A wave leaped ghostly at the yard wall. John stooped in a pool of water, felt a fur-coated bundle lying there, dragged it over the threshold, slammed the door, and relit the lamp.

Then he stared at the fur-coated bundle. It was a young seal; its eyes were glazed, its hinder feet curled up, and its foreflippers sprawling. 'Dead and gone!' thought John. 'And a while back so prettily playing! I guarantee your mammy told you to keep clear of the breakers. But youth is headstrong – and see what comes of it!' He shook his head and stooped to run his hand over the grey, sodden body.

Hullo, hullo! What was this? The body gave a hump and a wriggle under John's caressing hand; a flipper waggled, the lack-lustre eyes kindled. The young seal was looking up at John Pettigrew with eyes of unutterable wisdom.

'Oh, well, come on then, if that's the case, little fellow!' A delighted John lifted the seal in his arms and laid it carefully in front of the fire.

It was a merry evening they spent after that, John and his new companion. The little seal drank milk from a bottle, and ate the fish that was meant for John's supper. And John, remembering that seals are fond of music, played it a tune on his mouth-organ, and the little fellow clapped with his flippers, and bleated for more. More milk, or more fish, or more tunes? John couldn't be sure; so he plied it with all three.

And then they both fell asleep, the seal on the hearthrug, and John on the settle; for this was the first house-companion he had ever possessed, and he didn't feel like going upstairs and leaving it lonesome.

But, in his dreams, an old seal came to him, and the tears were flowing from her eyes in silver streams; and it seemed to John that if he didn't stop the flow of those tears they would presently drown the whole world. So, in the morning, when the wind had dropped, and the sea heaved grey and sullen, as if in sulky apology for the havoc it had caused, John carried his new friend through the wreckage in his yard, and over the bricks of fallen chimneys and the slates of torn roofs out in the street, and among piles of blown sand and great heaps of stones and seaweed, down to the shore, and there he pushed the little fellow out into the sea.

The little fellow spun round and round like a rudderless boat, as if it had forgotten which way to steer itself. And then it struggled out of the water and bleated after John; and when John turned for home, the little fellow came flipping and humping up the sand so fast that it reached the yard gate as soon as John did. So then John borrowed a boat, and rowed a long way out to sea, and dropped the little fellow gently overboard – and there was the little fellow spinning round and round once more, and crying out so loud that half the town could hear it. And so pitiful was its cry that John was obliged to take it into the boat again.

It came into John's mind, then, that perhaps the young seal was still suffering in some way from the

bang the breakers had given it, and that it didn't feel able to fend for itself: 'If only I could catch a glimpse of your mammy,' he said, 'I should know what to do.' He looked this way and that over the sparkling water, but all he saw was a couple of gulls, circling and mewing. 'Seal, mammy seal!' he called. But there was no answer.

'I don't know what may be in her mind – exactly,' said John. 'But I do think I'll have to care for you a while longer.' And with that he pulled for home; whilst the young seal lay contentedly in the bottom of the boat, and watched him with its wise eyes.

'Now,' said Sarah Polgraine, 'you can shoot the creature; and I'll make me a fur tippet for Sundays.'

'I've never handled a gun in my life,' said John with a chuckle. 'And I don't intend to handle one now.'

So then Sarah, who coveted the sealskin, carried on alarmingly; and said that John couldn't keep an outlandish creature like that about the place, and that if he was afraid to handle a gun he could use a sharp knife. And it came into John's mind, then, that though both he and Sarah were looking at the little seal, yet they were seeing different things. *She* was seeing a fur tippet, and *he* was seeing a dearly loved child. So he told her his dream about the tears that might presently drown the whole world, and Sarah said 'Stuff and nonsense!' But it seemed to John that the young seal understood, and nodded its head in approval. He went into the yard, cleared up the mess that the storm had made, and set to work again; and the little seal watched him with its shining eyes. And when John crossed the yard, it crossed the yard; and when John sat at his trade, it lay at his feet; and when John played on his mouth-organ, it made happy sounds and clapped with its flippers; and when John threw a ball, it caught the ball on its nose,

and spun it up and caught it again, which was very pretty to watch; and in the evenings it lay on the hearthrug and gazed at the fire; and so things went on for some days.

But John, much as he joyed in the company of his little friend, couldn't get the dream of an old seal with tear-streaming eyes out of his mind; and every day, when his work was done, he went down to the shore and looked into the grey, or the green, or the blue water for sight of the one who had shed those tears. And the little seal went with him, but it looked at John, and not at the water.

And then, one day, through a wave green and clear as glass John saw the shape of a swimmer; and up came a round, glistening head, turning this way and that, as if in search of something. 'There's your mammy at last,' said John; 'and it's into the water you go, my beauty, and no nonsense this time!'

And, so saying, he picked the little fellow up, and waded out as far as he could, and flung his playmate from him. Then he made a run for dry ground, and hid behind a rock, with just his head poked out to watch what would happen. And first there was the young seal spinning round and round like a rudderless boat, and crying after John; and then, out to sea, there was the old seal reared upright through a green wave and calling after the young one; and then there was the young one swimming out towards the green wave; and then there was nothing but the tossing water; and then a lifting wave bore the shapes of two swimmers in its bosom, and, as they floated up on the wave's crest, John saw their big eyes shining.

And now there was John going home, rejoicing that he had done right, but with a lonely feeling in his heart.

And is that the end of the story? No, indeed!

Though it has taken some time in the telling, it is only the beginning; and what follows is what you may believe or not believe, as you will.

Next Sunday, John took a walk by the sea-shore. He wasn't exactly looking for the seals, you understand, but he was thinking about them – picturing to himself what life would be like in the deep places of ocean, and of the things to be seen there, which no man has ever seen. And, all of a sudden, the thought came to him that man knew but little, and thought less, of the strangeness and power and glory of creation, and he took his mouth-organ out of his pocket and began to play a hymn. Well, he hadn't played more than a bar of that hymn when, down in the bright water just beneath him, he saw the old seal swimming, and balancing something on her nose. It wasn't a ball; but what it was John could not tell, for as she tossed it up and caught it again, it spun so quickly, and flashed so magnificently, that it made John's eyes water to look at it. And then – whizz! – it was flying through the air towards John, and he caught it in his two hands.

It was a small round mirror – and such a mirror! The frame was fashioned like a garland of flowers, and the heart of each flower was a great pearl, the petals were rubies and sapphires, and the leaves emeralds. John turned it this way and that in admiration, till it chanced that he turned it so that its glass reflected the sea, and there beneath him he saw, not a seal, but a beautiful woman with a child in her arms. The child wore a little crown of gold, and he stretched out his arms and waved to John, and the woman smiled at John very sweetly, and then they both disappeared under the water. And John stood staring into the mirror as if he couldn't believe his eyes.

He slanted the mirror to the sky, and saw the clouds; they *were* clouds, you understand, and yet they were also palaces and towers, and great white swans, and majestic old men in snowy garments. He slanted the mirror to the earth, and saw the flowers and the bushes; they *were* flowers and bushes, but the stems of the flowers were birds, and the leaves were wings, and every branch was a king with a jewelled crown. 'Oh,' thought John, as he made for home, 'I shall never be tired of looking in *this* mirror!' And, looking into it once again, he chanced to see his own face reflected; and he tucked the mirror hastily into his pocket, for he was almost ashamed to look at the glory and brightness, the majesty and beauty, of the lordly one who gazed kindly back at him.

Over against the sea wall he passed a group of old men, in their Sunday clothes, lounging to watch the water; some of them were squinny, some pot-bellied and bandy, some sad, some foolish. 'I wonder now,' thought John, 'what the mirror will make of this lot!' So he took it out of his pocket and slanted it upon them. And there they were – lords of the earth, every one of them: strong and straight, and handsome and brave, and dressed fit for the Kingdom of Heaven.

'If that's the way it is,' said John to himself, 'not only I, but the whole of the town, would be better for a peep into the mirror.' And he got a strong nail and hung the mirror on his front door, which was always shut, because he never went in that way.

You may be sure there was soon a crowd round the door, everyone jostling and pushing to have a look at themselves. Nobody knew quite what to make of what they saw: giddy girls came up, and looked and went away hushed and awestruck; old men and women looked, and walked down the street holding their heads high and smiling to themselves; young men looked, and walked off proud and solemn as

priests at a sacrifice. And in the dawn, when the street was empty, a thief came by, and coveted the frame for its precious stones; but, as he reached to unhook the mirror from its nail, he saw his face reflected, and it was the face of an angel. So he left the mirror where it was, and tiptoed away; because, of course, angels are not thieves.

It would take too long to tell of all the people who looked into John Pettigrew's mirror, and of what they saw there; but be sure that whoever looked saw nothing but beauty and goodness, because there was nothing else to see. And it wasn't long before there wasn't an evil, or a selfish, or a sick, or an angry person left in the town; because everyone remembered what they were really like, and behaved accordingly. The prison was empty, the law courts were turned into a dancing school, and the policemen, after yawning for a while at street corners, got tired of doing nothing, and took to growing strawberries. The mayor, by common consent, was left in authority; and if any citizen for a moment forgot himself and behaved foolishly, the mayor had but to order that he take a peep into John Pettigrew's mirror, and after that there was no more trouble with him.

There was only one person in the town who wasn't quite happy, and that was Sarah Polgraine. She was so used to grumbling and complaining, scolding and finding fault, that now, when everything was perfect and there was nobody left to find fault with, she felt like a pricked bubble. For what was the use of her having lived such an exemplary life, and worked herself to skin and bone, and done so much for John Pettigrew and a host of others, if it didn't give her the satisfaction of knowing herself to be more virtuous than anybody else in the town? All this nonsense about reflections in a mirror! *She* knew what people were like, and she knew what she was like, without any lying mirror to tell her! And so, every time she passed John Pettigrew's front door, Sarah Polgraine shut her eyes. For it seemed to her that the mirror had robbed her of her one pleasure in life.

That was an unhappy feeling to live with; and the unhappy feeling grew and grew, until there was no putting up with it. So one winter morning, when the wind was blowing half a hurricane, and the sea was grey and angry, she rose with the first streak of daylight, and ran to John Pettigrew's house; and, shutting her eyes, unhooked the mirror, tucked it under her shawl, and went and stood on a rock by the sea-shore, to throw the tiresome thing back to the deep places where it had come from. The wind was blowing so hard that she nearly lost her balance, but she raised her arm and threw; and there was the mirror now, flashing out over the water with its myriad-coloured jewels agleam in the rising sun. But, just as it left her hand, it happened that Sarah Polgraine for the first time saw her face reflected in it; and though it was but for a spinning second that she saw that face, certainly it was not the face of a woman who could do such an evil thing, and she began to weep bitterly, and cried out in a loud voice: 'Oh, what have I done? Give it back! Give it back!'

Then the round, glistening head of the old seal appeared on the top of a wave, balancing the mirror on her nose; and first she spun the mirror up and caught it, and then she gave it a toss and sent it flying back over the water to Sarah Polgraine.

Sarah Polgraine stretched out her hands; but what with the tears that were streaming from her eyes, and the wind that was blowing her hair across them, she couldn't see anything clearly, and, instead of catching the mirror, she let it slip through her fingers. It was dashed against the rock, and broke into a hundred pieces.

Sarah Polgraine scrambled off the rock and set up such a loud wailing that soon half the town was on the sea-shore. Some began to gather up the splinters, and they were the sensible ones, for in the fragments that they picked up they could still see, though cracked and piecemeal, the image of their glory reflected. Others began to blame Sarah Polgraine; and, as soon as they did that, she began to justify herself, and clean forgot the face she had seen for

one spinning second in the mirror. And soon the place was echoing with angry voices and hot words, such as had not been heard in the town for many a long day. One man picked up the jewelled frame and said he would have that, anyway; but another tried to wrench it from him, and then there were blows, as well as angry words. Hitting and snarling, the two of them fell off the rock into the sea, and there might have been murder done, had not a policeman, peacefully at work on the strawberry bed in his back garden, heard the racket and come running to take up his official duties once again.

And so, it wasn't very long before the townspeople went back to their old ways, as if no such thing as a mirror from the unsearchable deep had ever hung outside John Pettigrew's door to show them a different image of themselves: the quarrelsome quarrelled, the drunkards drank, the giglots giggled, and the thieves stole; the law courts were reopened, and the policemen put on their helmets and stood at street corners. In fact, as Sarah Polgraine said, it was shameful the way people went on, and what the world was coming to she *couldn't* think!

Only the sensible ones, John Pettigrew amongst them, cherished each his piece of broken mirror and, by taking a peep into it now and then, carried the image of a lordly one in their minds, and in their hearts.

Yes, that's the end of the story; except that whenever, as a young girl, things went criss-crossed with me and life seemed all awry, my grandmother, who was a wise and peace-loving old body, would smile and shake her head over my glum face, and say, 'Ah, child, you'd think differently if you could take a peep into John Pettigrew's mirror.'

Inside the story

When you have heard the story told:

In pairs or groups

1 Talk about the story and recall any bits you particularly liked – any words, phrases, descriptions, ideas . . .

2 At first there seem to be two quite separate stories here – one about the seal and one about the mirror. Talk about how the two stories are linked and whether it would make any difference if the second story (about the mirror) was told without any mention of the seal pup and its mother.

3 What are the main differences in character and outlook between John Pettigrew and Sarah Polgraine? Make a note of anything that tells us about how each of them sees the world.

4 Talk about exactly what it is that the mirror does and why it has the effect it has on people.

5 Do you think John or Sarah has the truer vision of how people are? Discuss why you think as you do.

6 Decide whether you think the story has a message or a moral and, if so, what you think it might be.

Different groups might like to think about the different questions above and then come together as a class to share their thoughts.

7 Imagine that the local and then the national press and television hear of the magic mirror in John Pettigrew's town. What happens?
- Who would they want to speak to and what questions would they ask?
- Would they get similar replies from all the townsfolk?
- Would they be pleased to find a town where everybody was good and happy? Why do you think they would or would not?
- What might happen to some reporters who looked in the magic mirror?
- Would newspapers change if the effect was to become widespread over the whole country?

On your own

We know what effect the magic mirror had on the people of the town. Imagine that a similar mirror appears in your neighbourhood, or in your school. Write a story about what happens.

LUTEY AND THE MERMAID
Susan Price

In Curey, in Cornwall, there once lived a man named Lutey. He made his living, in the main, as a fisherman, although he grew vegetables in a small garden beside his cottage, and was not above robbing a wrecked ship, coming home with oranges and lemons in his shirt, or rolling a cask of doubly-salted butter along the beach, or carrying a small keg of wine on his shoulder. Sometimes, too, he would bring home a half-drowned passenger or ship's boy, for although quick to make a profit out of the disaster if he could, he was a kind man, who always gave what help he could to anyone in trouble.

One day, after a bad storm, Lutey was wandering along the beach, looking to see if the storm had washed up anything worth bending down to pick up, since the sea was still too rough for him to go fishing. His little mongrel dog was running in circles round him, coming back whenever he saw his master stop, to sniff at what had been found. Lutey picked up a couple of coins, and some bottles which he thought he would wash out and sell, and then, in a pool of sea-water formed by some rocks, he found a mermaid. He stood and looked at her for a long time, while his dog yapped from a safe distance. Lutey knew that she was a mermaid by the long, strong, coiling tail, all silver and blue, which formed her body from the waist down. Above the waist – well; she was more beautiful than the most beautiful woman Lutey had ever seen. His own wife had been pretty enough for anyone when he had married her, but even combed and washed, and dressed in her best, she had not looked like this creature. His wife's skin was brown and red; the mermaid's was white, absolutely white; as white as the full moon on a clear night. His wife's eyes and hair were dark brown, like his own; the mermaid's hair was almost as white as her skin, but as the wind lifted first one strand and then another, green and blue and yellow lights flickered through it; and her eyes were large and grey. Over all the years Lutey's wife had grown stocky and almost shapeless with keeping house for him, and having his children; and although, when he had married her, Lutey had known this would happen, and although he loved her none the less for it, yet he was held by the sight of the mermaid's heart-breakingly slender arms and neck, and he shook his head in wonder and astonishment, and

hoped that he would never forget one line or colour of the sight.

At last the mermaid, who had been staring at him and winding long strands of her hair round her fingers, stretched out her beautiful arms to him, and said, 'The storm washed me up here, lad; wouldst carry me back?'

Lutey started at the sound of her voice, but then grinned through his beard, and said, 'Aye; I reckon I could carry a little thing like thee down to the water, even if it is a mile out;' and he climbed into the pool, and lifted the mermaid in his arms. She put her arms about his neck, coiled her long tail round his waist, and laid her head against his shoulder. 'Parson wouldn't like this if he could see it,' Lutey said, 'but he can't, and I shan't tell him.' And he began to carry the mermaid over the long stretch of sand to the sea's edge. His little dog ran after him.

'Thou'rt a good man,' said the mermaid, and rubbed her cold cheek against his beard. 'If I could grant wishes, and I said I would give thee three, what wouldst wish for, lad?'

'That would take some thinking about,' Lutey said.

'Think, then, love,' said the mermaid.

'Well . . .' said Lutey. 'Well . . . there's a lot suffer from aches and pains, especially in this cold weather. I know my poor old gel does, and it catches me sharp sometimes, in the back, when I bend – and then there's fevers, and coughs and colds and all sorts. Aye; I reckon I'd wish for the power to heal if I was going to wish. That'd do some good for a lot of folk, that would.'

'And the second wish?'

'Well . . . folk lose a lot of things, and most of 'em bain't got that much that they can afford to lose it; so I'd wish next for the power to discover things lost. That'd be a help.'

'And the third wish, love?'

'Well . . . Those other wishes wouldn't be much help if they died with me, would they? Not that I'm old, but I'm getting on. So, I'd wish that the powers could pass down to my sons and daughters. Aye; that I would.'

He felt a coldness on his cheek as the mermaid kissed him. 'Thou'rt a good man,' she said. 'As good as thou'rt handsome.' And she kissed him three times more; on the eyelid, on the neck and on the lips.

'Hey, hey, hey,' Lutey said. 'Madam! I hope my old gel bain't looking this way. I got to go back to her, tha knowst.'

'Come with me instead,' said the mermaid, and clung to him more tightly. 'Come with me, love. You sail over the water in your boats, you men; hast never wondered what lies beneath it? Deep, deep beneath?'

'I have wondered,' said Lutey; 'but I should drown.'

'I wouldn't let thee drown, lad,' said the mermaid. 'I'd take thee where no man that breathes air has ever been; and I'd love thee.'

Lutey reached the edge of the sea, and, shaking his head, he waded into it, carrying the mermaid to where the water was deep enough for her to swim away. 'I can't come,' he said.

The mermaid tightened her arms and tail about him with frightening strength. 'Come with me, and be my love,' she said. 'Come with me and see the sunken ships with their sails all torn into rags and drifting with the tides; come and see what they were carrying, all spilt, all spoilt; come and search for coins in the sand down there, Lutey, my Handsome; come and dig for lost rings and broken necklaces; and for every precious stone you find, I'll give you another kiss.' And she kissed him again, with a touch even colder than before; a cold that struck him through, and yet was strangely pleasant, exciting; thrilling. And if he had wondered before what lay beneath the sea and its changing colours, now he wondered and longed to know, ten times more.

'Why stay here above the lovely water?' the mermaid asked, as she stroked his hair. 'Why suffer the storms and the pains; why work and worry, and run after every little thing that might put a crumb in your mouth? We don't live so under the sea: we never worry about what might happen; we never worry about food; we have no needs. Let go, my love; let go of your sorry world; come with me; sink with me into the darkness. Oh come with me, Lutey; come with me, love; be my love, Sweet; come with me.'

Lutey shivered as her cold kisses stole the strength from him, and he sank to his knees in the water. The sea rushed up against his chest and splashed about the mermaid. He opened his mouth, and was about to say that he would go with her, when, from the edge of the sea came the sound of his little dog barking. The mermaid, startled, loosened her hold, and Lutey looked round.

Beyond the noisy little dog he saw the beach he had walked along that morning; and beyond the beach he saw the small, poor cottage where he lived. He saw smoke rising from holes in the roof; he saw his wife in the vegetable garden, stooping to pull something up; and he saw three of his children running, one after another, on to the beach. He knew then that he could not go with the mermaid, and he felt such sorrow at that, and for the dwindling, wasted life of his wife, and for the lives of his children which were yet to waste, that he felt a pain as if a knife had been driven into him, and tears came into his eyes. 'Oh, Sea-maid,' he said. 'I would come – I would come – but look, dost see my old gel back there? My poor old gel; if I go with thee, who's to dig the garden for her when her back aches, and get the vegetables in for next year? See the holes in the roof? Who'd mend 'em? See the smoke? Who'd chop the wood for the fire? Who'd find the money to feed and clothe the little uns if I wasn't here? No; my old gel she's too old now to do any better for herself than me, and I've got to stay and look after her.'

The mermaid wrapped her arms tightly round his neck, lashed out with her tail, and dragged him beneath the water. But Lutey was a strong man, and the water was not yet very deep. He struggled, and brought his head into the air again; and he dragged his knife from his belt and held it before the mermaid's face, knowing that all such creatures are afraid of cold iron; and he said, 'Go, in God's name!'

The water turned foamy and white all round him as the mermaid swam away; but at a distance she rose from the water again, and she called, 'Thou'rt a good man, Lutey, and each one of thy three wishes shall be granted. I prophesy, too, that neither thee nor any of thy children, nor thy children's children, nor any born of thy line shall ever, from this day, be hungry or cold. But thou art mine, Lutey, and I shall have thee. I grant thee nine more years to live in the air, and then I shall come and fetch thee home, lad.' Then she sank beneath the water, and Lutey waded back from the sea to his family.

Within a few days he had a chance to test the truth of the mermaid's words, for his youngest child fell sick, and could not sleep; but after Lutey had stroked her head and kissed her, she did sleep, and woke cured. It soon spread, from house to house, and village to village, that Lutey of Curey could heal, and people began to come to him when they were in pain, or feverish, or had wounds which had turned bad, or sores, or coughing-fits; and Lutey's skill and touch always brought ease. When it became known that he could also discover things that were lost, still more people came to him, and they all brought payment in eggs, or cake, or milk, or cheese, and sometimes in money, fulfilling the mermaid's prophecy that Lutey's children would never again be cold or hungry.

On the ninth anniversary of the day he had found the mermaid, Lutey went fishing, taking with him one of his youngest sons, a boy barely eight years old, who already possessed some of his father's powers. They fished all day, made a good catch, and,

as the light was beginning to fade, and they were thinking of putting back to shore, the mermaid suddenly rose from the water near the boat, stretched out her lovely arms, and called Lutey's name.

Lutey immediately stood, and moved as though to jump overboard. His son, though very frightened, was quick enough to reach out and clutch at his father's legs. Lutey looked down at him impatiently. 'I stayed then,' he said. 'Now let me go.' The boy released him in bewilderment, and Lutey threw himself into the sea. He sank, and did not rise, for the mermaid dragged him down with her.

Lutey's son was left alone in the still rocking boat, the air growing cold and dark over the sea. He rowed home alone without his father, and no trace of Lutey was ever seen after that; neither his body, nor his clothes, nor anything belonging to him was ever washed up for mortals to find.

Lutey's son grew, and came into all the powers his father had had; and others of his own, for after he had seen the mermaid take his father, he always looked so hard for what was not to be seen that at last he saw its shadows – moving shadows at the edges and corners of rooms; shadows among trees and stone field-walls of the land, and among the rocks of the beach; shadows miming what was yet to happen.

But he never lived to have children, this second-sighted Lutey, for he still followed his father's trade of fisherman, and nine years after his father's disappearance, he went fishing with his younger brother; and the mermaid rose from the water and called to him. Without a word, without any hesitation, Young Lutey swung himself over the boat's side into her arms, and sank with her into the deep, cold sea.

His brother lived to marry, and his children inherited the family's gifts, as did their children, and indeed, for many generations there were no healers in Cornwall so famous as the Luteys of Curey; but every nine years the mermaid rose from the water and called for her payment; and another Lutey was drowned.

Inside the story

When you have heard the story read aloud:

In pairs or groups

1 Talk about the story and recall any parts you particularly liked – any words, phrases, descriptions, ideas . . .

2 Lutey feels very attracted to the mermaid – she tempts him with what she calls love. What other temptations does she offer him?

3 What do we learn about Lutey's character from his choice to go back to his wife and family, and from his three wishes?

On your own

The mermaid describes some of the wonders of the world beneath the sea. We are given hints of what it is like – sunken ships, coins in the sand, rings and necklaces . . . Imagine you are Lutey or his son, plunging for the first time into the watery kingdom: describe what you see. Maybe you could draw a picture to illustrate your ideas.

The next story is a traditional English tale. Angela Carter, who collected this story in *The Virago Book of Fairy Tales*, remarks that the story of Mr Fox, which is also known in the USA, was already ancient 'when the first English settlers took their invisible cargo of stories and songs across the Atlantic in the sixteenth and seventeenth centuries'. She reminds us that Benedick, a character in Shakespeare's play, *Much Ado About Nothing*, which was written in about 1599, refers to Mr Fox's words. In Act I scene i he says:

'Like the old tale, my Lord, it is not so, nor 'twas not so, but, indeed, God forbid it should be so.'

Mr Fox is, be warned, very bloody and not for the fainthearted. Like all such stories, it needs to be read aloud and relished. Passed down from generation to generation, it has the true rhythms of the storyteller's art; centuries of telling and retelling have shaped it. Hear it read aloud and join in at the words in italics.

MR FOX
Angela Carter

Lady Mary was young, and Lady Mary was fair. She had two brothers, and more lovers than she could count. But of them all, the bravest and most gallant, was a Mr Fox, whom she met when she was down at her father's country house. No one knew who Mr Fox was; but he was certainly brave, and surely rich, and of all her lovers, Lady Mary cared for him alone. At last it was agreed upon between them that they should be married. Lady Mary asked Mr Fox where they should live, and he described to her his castle, and where it was; but, strange to say, did not ask her, or her brothers, to come and see it.

So one day, near the wedding day, when her brothers were out, and Mr Fox was away for a day or two on business, as he said, Lady Mary set out for Mr Fox's castle. And after many searchings, she came at last to it, and a fine strong house it was, with high walls and a deep moat. And when she came up to the gateway she saw written on it:

Be bold, be bold.

But as the gate was open, she went through it, and found no one there. So she went up to the doorway, and over it she found written:

Be bold, be bold, but not too bold.

Still she went on, till she came into the hall, and went up the broad stairs till she came to a door in the gallery, over which was written:

Be bold, be bold, but not too bold,
Lest that your heart's blood should run cold.

But Lady Mary was a brave one, she was, and she opened the door, and what do you think she saw? Why, bodies and skeletons of beautiful young ladies all stained with blood. So Lady Mary thought it was high time to get out of that horrid place, and she closed the door, went through the gallery, and was just going down the stairs, and out of the hall, when who should she see through the window, but Mr Fox dragging a beautiful young lady along from the gateway to the door. Lady Mary rushed downstairs, and hid herself behind a cask, just in time, as Mr Fox came in with the poor young lady who seemed to have fainted. Just as he got near Lady Mary, Mr Fox saw a diamond ring glittering on the finger of the young lady he was dragging, and he tried to pull it off. But it was tightly fixed, and would not come off, so Mr Fox cursed and swore, and drew his sword, raised it, and brought it down upon the hand of the poor lady. The sword cut off the hand, which jumped up into the air, and fell of all places in the world into Lady Mary's lap. Mr Fox looked about a bit, but did not think of looking behind the cask, so at last he went on dragging the young lady up the stairs into the Bloody Chamber.

As soon as she heard him pass through the gallery, Lady Mary crept out of the door, down through the gateway, and ran home as fast as she could.

Now it happened that the very next day the marriage contract of Lady Mary and Mr Fox was to be signed, and there was a splendid breakfast before that. And when Mr Fox was seated at table opposite Lady Mary, he looked at her. 'How pale you are this morning, my dear.' 'Yes,' said she, 'I had a bad night's rest last night. I had horrible dreams.' 'Dreams go by contraries,' said Mr Fox; 'but tell us your dream, and your sweet voice will make the time pass till the happy hour comes.'

'I dreamed,' said Lady Mary, 'that I went yestermorn to your castle, and I found it in the woods, with high walls, and a deep moat, and over the gateway was written:

Be bold, be bold.'

'But it is not so, nor it was not so,' said Mr Fox.

'And when I came to the doorway over it was written:

Be bold, be bold, but not too bold.'

'It is not so, nor it was not so,' said Mr Fox.
'And then I went upstairs, and came to a gallery, at the end of which was a door, on which was written:

Be bold, be bold, but not too bold,
Lest that your heart's blood should run cold.'

'It is not so, nor it was not so,' said Mr Fox.
'And then – and then I opened the door, and the room was filled with bodies and skeletons of poor dead women, all stained with their blood.'
'It is not so, nor it was not so. And God forbid it should be so,' said Mr Fox.
'I then dreamed that I rushed down the gallery, and just as I was going down the stairs, I saw you, Mr Fox, coming up to the hall door, dragging after you a poor young lady, rich and beautiful.'
'It is not so, nor it was not so. And God forbid it should be so,' said Mr Fox.
'I rushed downstairs, just in time to hide myself behind a cask, when you, Mr Fox, came in dragging the young lady by the arm. And, as you passed me, Mr Fox, I thought I saw you try and get off her diamond ring, and when you could not, Mr Fox, it seemed to me in my dream, that you out with your sword and hacked off the poor lady's hand to get the ring.'
'It is not so, nor it was not so. And God forbid it should be so,' said Mr Fox, and was going to say something else as he rose from his seat, when Lady Mary cried out:

'But it is so, and it was so. Here's hand and ring I have to show,' and pulled out the lady's hand from her dress, and pointed it straight at Mr Fox.

At once her brothers and her friends drew their swords and cut Mr Fox into a thousand pieces.

Inside the story

When you have heard the story read aloud:

In pairs or groups

1 How did *you* think the story would end? Which parts did you like best? Share your feelings about it.

2 The story is full of repeated phrases (*'Be bold . . .'*, 'It is not so . . .'*) Look back at these and see how many you can

What effect does this repetition have on the way we read the story and how it makes us feel?

3 In groups of three (Storyteller, Mr Fox, Lady Mary) rehearse a reading of the story to present to the rest of the class. You may find it helps if you leave out the phrases 'said she', 'said Mr Fox', etc. when you dramatise the story in this way. The voices should tell your audience which character is speaking.
  If you prefer, you might choose to tape-record your

version as a radio programme, or you might like to think about acting it out. One way of combining both elements is to have the story mimed by one group while the voices of another group tell the story. If you are feeling more ambitious, you can move on to using a drama room with appropriate lighting, sound effects and music.

On your own

Devise a storyboard version of the tale. To do this, you first have to decide what you think are the most important scenes in the story. There may be as many as twelve or more of these. Then you must decide how you will illustrate each scene in a single small picture. Divide your page up into equal sized boxes, one for each scene, and draw your pictures. You can add words in speech bubbles from the characters' mouths and you can write a few words beneath each picture as well. Although a storyboard *can* be produced on an A4 size sheet, a double size sheet (A3) is probably easier to work on.

The next story is a tale about a modern ghost, one you might meet when you are out shopping or coming home from school. It is quite bloodless, but there is something rather chilling about the thought of meeting ghosts in everyday life in broad daylight. And that's not the only strange thing about it – the storyteller is rather unusual too.

A Grave Misunderstanding

Leon Garfield

I am a dog. I think you ought to know right away. I don't want to save it up for later, because you might begin to wonder what sort of a person it was who went about on all fours, sniffing at bottoms and peeing up against lampposts in the public street. You wouldn't like it; and I don't suppose you'd care to have anything more to do with me.

The truth of the matter is, we have different standards, me and my colleagues, that is; not in everything, I hasten to bark, but in enough for it to be noticeable. For instance, although we are as fond of a good walk as the next person, love puppies and smoked salmon, we don't go much on reading. We find it hard to turn the pages. But, on the other paw, a good deep snoutful of mingled air as it comes humming off a rubbish dump can be as teasing to us as a sonnet. Indeed, there are rhymes in rancid odours such as you'd never dream of; and every puddle tells a story.

We see things, too. Only the other day, when me and my Person were out walking, and going as brisk as biscuits, through that green and quiet place of marble trees and stony, lightless lampposts, where people bury their bones and never dig them up, I saw a ghost. I stopped. I glared, I growled, my hair stood up on end –

'What the devil's the matter with you now?' demanded my Person.

'What a beautiful dog!' said the ghost, who knew that I knew what she was, and that we both knew that my Person did not.

She was the lifeless, meaningless shell of a young female person whose bones lay not very far away. No heart beat within her, there was wind in her veins, and she smelled of worm-crumble and pine.

'Thank you,' said my Person, with a foolishly desiring smile: for the ghost's eyes were very come-hitherish, even though her hither was thither, under the grass. 'He *is* rather a handsome animal. Best of breed at Cruft's you know.' The way to his heart was always open through praise of me.

'Does he bite?' asked the ghost, watching me with all the empty care of nothingness trying to be something.

'SHE'S DEAD – SHE'S DEAD!'

'Stop barking!' said my Person. 'Don't be frightened. He wouldn't hurt a fly. Do you come here often?'

'Every day,' murmured the ghost, with a sly look towards her bones. She moved a little nearer to my Person. A breeze sprang up, and I could smell it blowing right through her, like frozen flowers. 'He looks very fierce,' said the ghost. 'Are you sure that he's kind?'

'COME AWAY – COME AWAY!'

'Stop barking!' commanded my Person, and looked at the ghost with springtime in his eyes. If only he could have smelled the dust inside her head, and heard the silence inside her breast! But it was no good. All he could see was a silken smile. He was only a person, and blindly trusted his eyes . . .

'Dogs,' said the ghost, 'should be kept on a lead in the churchyard. There's a notice on the gate.' She knew that I knew where she was buried, and that I'd just been going to dig up her bones.

My Person obeyed; and the ghost looked at me as if to say, 'Now you'll never be able to show him that I'm dead!'

'SHE'S COLD! SHE'S EMPTY! SHE'S GRANDDAUGHTER DEATH!'

'Stop barking!' shouted my Person, and, dragging me after, walked on, already half in love with the loveless ghost.

We passed very close to her bones. I could smell them, and I could hear the little nibblers dryly rustling. I pulled, I strained, I jerked to dig up her secret . . .

'He looks so wild!' said the ghost. 'His eyes are rolling and his jaws are dripping. Are you sure he doesn't have a fever? Don't you think he ought to go to the vet?'

'He only wants to run off and play,' said my Person. 'Do you live near here?'

'YES! YES! RIGHT BY THAT MARBLE LAMPPOST! SIX PAWS DEEP IN THE EARTH!'

'Stop barking!' said my Person. 'Do you want to wake up the dead?'

The ghost started. Then she laughed, like the wind among rotting leaves. 'I have a room nearby,' she murmured. 'A little room all to myself. It is very convenient, you know.'

'A little room all to yourself?' repeated my Person, his heart beating with eager concern. 'How lonely that must be!'

'Yes,' she said. 'Sometimes it is very lonely in my little room, even though I hear people walking and talking upstairs, over my head.'

'Then let me walk back with you,' said my Person; 'and keep you company!'

'No dogs allowed,' said the ghost. 'They would turn me out, you know.'

'Then come my way!' said my Person; and the ghost raised her imitation eyebrows in imitation surprise. 'Madam will you walk,' sang my Person laughingly. 'Madam will you talk, Madam will you walk and talk with me?'

'I don't see why not,' smiled the ghost.

'BECAUSE SHE'S DEAD – DEAD – DEAD!'

'Stop barking!' said my Person. '"I will give you the keys of Heaven, I will give you the keys of my heart . . ."'

'The keys of Heaven?' sighed the ghost. 'Would you really?'

'And the keys of my heart! Will you have dinner with me?'

'Are you inviting me into your home?'

'NO GHOSTS ALLOWED! SHE'LL TURN ME OUT!'

'Stop barking! Yes . . . if you'd like to!'

'Oh, I would indeed – I would indeed!'

'DON'T DO IT! YOU'LL BE BRINGING DEATH INTO OUR HOME!'

'For God's sake, stop that barking! This way . . .

this way . . .'

It was hopeless, hopeless! There was only one thing left for a dog to do. *She* knew what it was, of course: she could see it in my eyes. She walked on the other side of my Person, and always kept him between herself and me. I bided my time . . .

'Do you like Italian food?' asked my Person.

'Not spaghetti,' murmured the ghost. 'It reminds me of worms.'

It was then that I broke free. I jerked forward with all my strength and wrenched the lead from out of my Person's grasp. He shouted! The ghost glared and shrank away. For a moment I stared into her eyes, and she stared into mine.

'Dogs must be kept on a lead!' whispered the ghost as I jumped. 'There's a notice on . . . on . . . on . . .'

It was like jumping through cobwebs and feathers; and when I turned, she'd vanished like a puff of air. I saw the grass shiver, and I knew she'd gone back to her bones.

'SHE WAS DEAD! SHE WAS DEAD! I TOLD YOU SO!'

My Person didn't answer. He was shaking, he was trembling; for the very first time, he couldn't believe his eyes.

'What happened? Where – where is she? Where has she gone?'

I showed him. Trailing my lead, I went to where she lay, six paws under, and began to dig.

'No! No!' he shrieked. 'For God's sake, let her lie there in peace!'

Thankfully I stopped. The earth under the grass was thick and heavy, and the going was hard. I went back to my Person. He had collapsed on a bench and was holding his head in his hands. I tried to comfort him by licking his ear.

A female person walked neatly by. She was young and smooth and shining, and smelled of coffee and cats. She was dressed in the softest of white.

'Oh, what a beautiful dog,' she said, pausing to admire me.

He stared up at her. His eyes widened; his teeth began to chatter. He could not speak.

'GO ON! GO ON! "BEST OF BREED AT CRUFTS'S!"'

'Hush!' said the female person, reproaching me with a gentle smile. 'You'll wake up the dead!'

'Is she real?' whispered my Person, his eyes as wide and round as tins. 'Or is she a ghost? Show me, show me! Try to jump through her like you did before! Jump, jump!'

'BUT SHE'S REAL! SHE'S ALIVE!'

'Stop barking and jump!'

So I jumped. She screamed – but not in fright. She screamed with rage. My paws were still thick and filthy with churchyard mud, and, in a moment, so was her dress.

'You – you madman!' she shouted at my shamefaced Person. 'You told him to do it! You told him to jump! You're not fit to have a dog!'

'But – but –' he cried out as she stormed away, to report him, she promised, to the churchyard authorities and the RSPCA.

'I TOLD YOU SHE WAS ALIVE! I TOLD YOU SO!'

'Stop barking!' wept my Person. 'Please!'

Inside the story

In pairs or groups

1 The story is told by a dog. Look carefully at the three opening paragraphs and jot down the ways in which the writer makes us (almost) believe this is possible. Think about how the dog addresses us; any words or phrases that reinforce the idea that we are seeing life from a dog's point of view; any unusual (to us) ways of seeing places.

2 The words and phrases used by the dog to describe the young woman's ghost are, in a way, rather poetic. Pick out these descriptions and jot them down.

We are told that the man was 'only a person, and blindly trusted his eyes'. Jot down the words and phrases describing the man's view of how he sees the young woman. How are the man's and the dog's views of the woman different?

3 How does the ghost try to deal with the threat posed by the dog?

4 What do you think the ghost wanted of the man?

5 Was the ending what you expected?

On your own

1 Although the story is told from the dog's point of view, we also get an impression of how the man and the ghost saw things. Think about how what happened might have appeared to the Person and to the ghost.

Rewrite the story, either from the Person's perspective or from the ghost's angle.

2 Write your own story concerning your 'Person' (not 'owner') from the point of view of another animal. Imagine, for example, that the story had begun 'I am a cat', or 'I am a parrot', or even 'I am a goldfish'. Each of these creatures has its own particular way of looking at the world and different things are important to each of them. Like the dog, each has its own distinctive voice, and perhaps its own way of speaking. Look again at the opening of this story for some ideas about how you could slip into the character of your chosen creature.

3
FROM FOUR TO FOURTEEN

The stories in this section are about young people, some of them *very* young and others nearer your own age.

Early on we are all storytellers. We sometimes find it difficult to distinguish fact from fiction and love 'making things up'. Early childhood is the time when children are perhaps at their most inventive and see the world partly as it is, partly as they wish it to be.

We are born into a world of marvels which may even include a strange man in red who travels the skies on a magical sleigh drawn by reindeer and who somehow manages to enter our homes by way of the chimney and leave us presents. If you believe that, you'll believe anything!

We begin the section with a 'story' by Sean Thomas, a four year old boy whose father was so taken with his stories that he wrote down exactly what Sean said.

WHAT HAPPENS AT SCHOOL
Sean Thomas

When I kiss Elizabeth
all the clothes dance
and all the boys jump up on the roof

                                       And

do you know what the dinner does?
The dinner comes down from the big school
then it lays itself on the tables
and eats itself up
Do you know what the plates do?
They gather themselves up
they go to Mrs Herd

they get into the washing-basin
they wash themselves
and they put themselves back on the shelves

                                          And

do you know what the pictures do?
They come down
throw the old ones in the fire
then the crayons get out
pull out a piece of paper
they draw another picture
then the sellotape comes out of the cupboard
and sticks the pictures up

                                          And

do you know what the school does?
The School pulls itself down
and builds itself up into a church

When I kiss Elizabeth
magic-stuff comes
out through our mouths

                                          And

do you know what the plants do?
They all die
then the seeds in the bag
come into the garden
then they pop into the ground

                                          And

do you know what the trees do?
They spring themselves down and die
the seeds walk about
in the mud
and the wind comes along and blows over them
and grows up into apple trees and
cherry trees grow up
then some sunflowers came
and tulips came
and roses came

                                          And and

do you know what the lights do?
They come down
the bulbs go to the shop
to buy another bulb
Do you know what the piano does?
The piano plays itself and
all the toys jump
and play with themselves

And

do you know what the sky does
All the sky jumps down
in the night it did
the sun fell the wind dropped   And
and half the world fell down and   And
all the flies were dead   And
and all the wasps were dead
no more flies and no more wasps

do you know what the plates do?
They gather themselves up . . .

Inside the story

In groups

1 Talk about Sean's story and the way he tells it. What is it about the way it is told that makes us immediately recognise that it is a young child speaking?

2 Do you remember similar stories you used to tell when you were little or is that time too far away? Do you know any small children who are still at that stage and who tell stories like this? The imaginary world of 'Play' can be almost more real than the real world to young children, and they sometimes have difficulty disentangling the two, taking both equally seriously and talking earnestly to themselves or even to imaginary friends. Share your experiences with the rest of the group.

On your own

If you are able to listen to a younger child telling stories in this way, perhaps you could jot down the kinds of things he or she says, like Sean's father. Even better, you might be able to tape-record what is said. An interesting time is just before bed when a child is sleepy and going over the day in his or her mind, 'scribble talking' towards sleep.

You might also find it interesting to ask the child to tell you a story, or to take a well-known story – a fairy tale, perhaps – and to ask the child to tell you about it. Does the child think it is true?

The story that follows, is about just such an occasion. A small boy named William listens to his Granny's story of the three pigs and constantly interrupts with his own version of what happened.

WILLIAM'S VERSION

Jan Mark

William and Granny were left to entertain each other for an hour while William's mother went to the clinic.

'Sing to me,' said William.

'Granny's too old to sing,' said Granny.

'I'll sing to you, then,' said William. William only knew one song. He had forgotten the words and the tune, but he sang it several times, anyway.

'Shall we do something else now?' said Granny.

'Tell me a story,' said William. 'Tell me about the wolf.'

'Red Riding Hood?'

'No, not *that* wolf, the other wolf.'

'Peter and the wolf?' said Granny.

'Mummy's going to have a baby,' said William.

'I know,' said Granny.

William looked suspicious.

'How do you know?'

'Well . . . she told me. And it shows, doesn't it?'

'The lady down the road had a baby. It looks like a pig,' said William. He counted on his fingers. 'Three babies looks like three pigs.'

'Ah,' said Granny. 'Once upon a time there were three little pigs. Their names were –'

'They didn't have names,' said William.

'Yes they did. The first pig was called –'

'Pigs don't have names.'

'Some do. These pigs had names.'

'No they didn't.' William slid off Granny's lap and went to open the corner cupboard by the fireplace. Old magazines cascaded out as old magazines do when they have been flung into a cupboard and the door slammed shut. He rooted among them until he found a little book covered with brown paper, climbed into the cupboard, opened the door, closed it and climbed out again. 'They didn't have names,' he said.

'I didn't know you could read,' said Granny, properly impressed.

'C – A – T, wheelbarrow,' said William.

'Is that the book Mummy reads to you out of?'

'It's my book,' said William.

'But it's the one Mummy reads?'

'If she says please,' said William.

'Well, that's Mummy's story, then. My pigs have names.'

'They're the wrong pigs.' William was not open to negotiation. 'I don't want them in this story.'

'Can't we have different pigs this time?'

'No. They won't know what to do.'

'Once upon a time,' said Granny, 'there were three little pigs who lived with their mother.'

'Their mother was dead,' said William.

'Oh, I'm sure she wasn't,' said Granny.

'She was dead. You make bacon out of dead pigs. She got eaten for breakfast and they threw the rind out for the birds.'

'So the three little pigs had to find homes for themselves.'

'No,' William consulted his book. 'They had to build little houses.'

'I'm just coming to that.'

'You said they had to *find* homes. They didn't *find* them.'

'The first little pig walked along for a bit until he met a man with a load of hay.'

'It was a lady.'

'A lady with a load of hay?'

'NO! It was a lady-pig. You said *he*.'

'I thought all the pigs were little boy-pigs,' said Granny.

'It says lady-pig here,' said William, 'It says the lady-pig went for a walk and met a man with a load of hay.'

'So the lady-pig,' said Granny, 'said to the man, "May I have some of that hay to build a house?" and the man said, "Yes." Is that right?'

'Yes,' said William. 'You know that baby?'

'What baby?'

'The one Mummy's going to have. Will that baby have shoes on when it comes out?'

'I don't think so,' said Granny.

'It will have cold feet,' said William.

'Oh no,' said Granny. 'Mummy will wrap it up in a soft shawl, all snug.'

'I don't *mind* if it has cold feet,' William explained. 'Go on about the lady-pig.'

'So the little lady-pig took the hay and built a little house. Soon the wolf came along and the wolf said –'

'You didn't tell where the wolf lived.'

'I don't know where the wolf lived.'

'15 Tennyson Avenue, next to the bomb-site,' said William.

'I bet it doesn't say that in the book,' said Granny, with spirit.

'Yes it does.'

'Let me see, then.'

William folded himself up with his back to Granny, and pushed the book up under his pullover.

'*I* don't think it says that in the book,' said Granny.

'It's in ever so small words,' said William.

'So the wolf said, "Little pig, little pig, let me come in," and the little pig answered, "No". So the wolf said, "Then I'll huff and I'll puff and I'll blow your house down," and he huffed and he puffed and he blew the house down, and the little pig ran away.'

'He ate the little pig,' said William.

'No, no,' said Granny. 'The little pig ran away.'

'He ate the little pig. He ate her in a sandwich.'

'All right, he ate the little pig in a sandwich. So the second little pig –'

'You didn't tell about the tricycle.'

'What about the tricycle?'

'The wolf got on his tricycle and went to the bread shop to buy some bread. To make the sandwich,' William explained, patiently.

'Oh, well, the wolf got on his tricycle and went to the bread shop to buy some bread. And he went to the grocer's to buy some butter.' This innovation did not go down well.

'He already had some butter in the cupboard,' said William.

'So then the second little pig went for a walk and met a man with a load of wood, and the little pig said to the man, "May I have some of that wood to build a house?" and the man said, "Yes."'

'He didn't say please.'

'"Please may I have some of that wood to build a house?"'

'It was sticks.'

'Sticks *are* wood.'

William took out his book and turned the pages. 'That's right,' he said.

'Why don't you tell the story?' said Granny.

'I can't remember it,' said William.

'You could read it out of your book.'

'I've lost it,' said William, clutching his pullover.

'Look, do you know who this is?' He pulled a green angora scarf from under the sofa.

'No, who is it?' said Granny, glad of the diversion.

'This is Doctor Snake.' He made a scarf wriggle across the carpet.

'Why is he a doctor?'

'Because he is all furry,' said William. He wrapped the doctor round his neck and sat sucking the loose end. 'Go on about the wolf.'

'So the little pig built a house of sticks and along came the wolf – on his tricycle?'

'He came by bus. He didn't have any money for a ticket so he ate up the conductor.'

'That wasn't very nice of him,' said Granny.

'No,' said William. 'It wasn't *very* nice.'

'And the wolf said, "Little pig, little pig, let me come in," and the little pig said, "No," and the wolf said, "Then I'll huff and I'll puff and I'll blow your house down," so he huffed and he puffed and he blew the house down. And then what did he do?' Granny asked, cautiously.

William was silent.

'Did he eat the second little pig?'

'Yes.'

'How did he eat this little pig?' said Granny, prepared for more pig sandwiches or possibly pig on toast.

'With his mouth,' said William.

'Now the third little pig went for a walk and met a man with a load of bricks. And the little pig said, "*Please* may I have some of those bricks to build a house?" and the man said, "Yes." So the little pig took the bricks and built a house.'

'He built it on the bomb-site.'

'Next door to the wolf?' said Granny. 'That was very silly of him.'

'There wasn't anywhere else,' said William. 'All the roads were full up.'

'The wolf didn't have to come by bus or tricycle this time, then, did he?' said Granny, grown cunning.

'Yes.' William took out the book and peered in, secretively. 'He was playing in the cemetery. He had to get another bus.'

'And did he eat the conductor this time?'

'No. A nice man gave him some money, so he bought a ticket.'

'I'm glad to hear it,' said Granny.

'He ate the nice man,' said William.

'So the wolf got off the bus and went up to the little pig's house, and he said, "Little pig, little pig, let me come in," and the little pig said, "No," and then the wolf said, "I'll huff and I'll puff and I'll blow your house down," and he huffed and he puffed and he huffed and he puffed but he couldn't blow the house down because it was made of bricks.'

'He couldn't blow it down,' said William, 'because it was stuck to the ground.'

'Well, anyway, the wolf got very cross then, and he climbed on the roof and shouted down the chimney, "I'm coming to get you!" but the little pig just laughed and put a big saucepan of water on the fire.'

'He put it on the gas stove.'

'He put it on the *fire*,' said Granny, speaking very rapidly, 'and the wolf fell down the chimney and into the pan of water and was boiled and the little pig ate him for supper.'

William threw himself full length on the carpet and screamed.

'He didn't! He didn't! *He didn't!* He didn't eat the wolf.'

Granny picked him up, all stiff and kicking, and sat him on her lap.

'Did I get it wrong again, love? Don't cry. Tell me what really happened.'

William wept, and wiped his nose on Doctor Snake.

'The little pig put the saucepan on the gas stove and the wolf got down the chimney and put the little pig in the saucepan and boiled him. He had him for tea, with chips,' said William.

'Oh,' said Granny. 'I've got it all wrong, haven't I? Can I see the book, then I shall know, next time.'

William took the book from under his pullover. Granny opened it and read, *First Aid for Beginners: a Practical Handbook*.

'I see,' said Granny. 'I don't think I can read this. I left my glasses at home. You tell Gran how it ends.'

William turned to the last page which showed a prostrate man with his leg in a splint; *compound fracture of the femur*.

'Then the wolf washed up and got on his tricycle and went to see his Granny, and his Granny opened the door and said, "Hello, William."'

'I thought it was the wolf.'

'It was. It was the wolf. His name was William Wolf,' said William.

'What a nice story,' said Granny, 'You tell it much better than I do.'

'I can see up your nose,' said William. 'It's all whiskery.'

Inside the story

In groups

Do you remember knowing stories and pretending to read them, being able to tell them before you could actually read them for yourself?

What sort of things does William do and say that we can recognise and that make him seem a real character?

Share your ideas with the rest of the class.

In pairs

Much of the story is written as conversation between William and his Granny. It is almost like a play. Working together with one of you as William and the other as Granny, dramatise the story as a radio play. To do this, you will need to look carefully through the story to see what pieces of description you will have to miss out, and think what sound effects and additional material you will need. For example, you will probably want sound effects for the pages of the book being turned, and for William throwing himself on the carpet and screaming. You will also probably decide to have Granny say the title of the book – *First Aid for Beginners: A Practical Handbook* – out loud, so that the audience knows exactly what William has been pretending to read from. As the story is quite long for one pair to dramatise by themselves, you may find it more manageable to split it into about four or five episodes and for different pairs to take responsibility for different sections. When you have rehearsed the play and made it as professional as you can, tape-record your version.

On your own

At the beginning, William says he doesn't want to hear the story of Red Riding Hood and that he would rather hear about the Three Pigs. Imagine that the next day he wants to hear Red Riding Hood or another fairy tale and write William's version of that story including whatever material you think he might have added. Try to tell the story mainly through conversation, as Jan Mark does.

Timothy Callender's story, 'An Assault on Santa Claus', is set in Barbados in the West Indies. The author was born and brought up there. He still lives, writes and teaches there.

AN ASSAULT ON SANTA CLAUS

Timothy Callender

When Barry first heard of Santa Claus, he was puzzled. He wanted to make sure that his grandfather had heard aright.

'You mean, you never know?' his grandfather asked. 'Santa Claus never bring nothing for you at Christmas yet?'

'No,' Barry said.

'Lord, boy, I could imagine how you does behave when you inside you parents home,' Grandfather said. 'Is only when you behave good that you can get any presents from Santa Claus.'

Barry nodded slowly.

'You must try and behave good this Christmas,' Grandfather said. 'I feel sure that if you behave good he may leave something for you when he pass through.'

'Is a whole lot of children he have to visit. You think he have enough toys for all of them?'

'Yes, man. Santa Claus always carry along the exact amount of toys.'

Barry thought about it all the Christmas season. He couldn't understand how Santa Claus would find out, but he made sure that he behaved himself. He was very obedient to all his grandfather said. Day by day he restrained himself from numerous temptations. He hoped that Santa was taking careful note of it all.

'You sure he know how good I behaving?' he asked his grandfather.

'Santa know what you deserve,' Grandfather said. 'You just wait and see if he don't bring the same carpentry set that you say you would like for Christmas.'

So Barry hoped, with the same fervour that he hoped Santa was noticing his good behaviour. All things considered, it was an easy way to gain a valuable gift.

It was a remarkable change. Grandfather was pleased. 'Why you can't behave so all the while?' he asked. 'Is the first time I ever see you so quiet and obedient. I hear all about how you was behaving before, you know. Your parents tell me how much trouble you always getting yourself into. They tell me how you always fighting at school, how you always getting licks, and how you involve yourself with the police and Probation Officer too. But look how nice you behaving now. Why you can't behave so all the while?'

'Is all them boys that does interfere with me first,' Barry muttered.

'I must tell yuh parents how well you behave all the time you spend vacation here with me.'

Barry nodded.

Christmas Eve came. Barry was in a state of suppressed excitement all day. Evening took long in coming.

'Tonight is the night,' Grandfather said at supper. 'You mustn't forget to put out something for Santa to drop presents in.'

'Is all right,' Barry said. 'I have a crocus bag tie onto the bedstead.'

Grandfather laughed. 'No boy. You can't make it look like you expect everything. A crocus bag look too greedy. Why you don't put a ordinary paper bag?'

'All right,' Barry said. But he didn't like it much. He had begun to feel that he had behaved well long enough to deserve more than a paper bag of gifts, even if the carpentry set was one of them. Santa had a whole big bag of gifts, and plenty more where they came from. He wondered how he could outwit Santa as he hung up his paper bag. Wondered if it was possible for Santa to make a mistake and give him more than he intended.

'We'll have to leave the window open,' he told Grandfather. 'We ain't have no chimney on this house.'

'Is all right,' Grandfather answered, and laughed. 'Is obvious to me that you never hear 'bout the things Santa can do. You ain't know he could even come through the keyhole?'

'He come just like a magic-man, then,' Barry said.

'You kin say so. But remember, he ain't going come unless you fall asleep, because he really don't like no children to see him.'

'All right, I going to bed now,' Barry said.

Grandfather smiled when he left. He know that Barry, like every other one of his grandsons, would stay awake to see Santa Claus.

Barry lay down without sleeping. His eyes were open but he was very still. He could hear his heartbeat sounding through the pillow. He heard the clock strike midnight. Santa must come sometime soon.

He had barely begun to doze when the sound of the door lock woke him. He stiffened. From where he lay he looked directly past his feet toward the door. The door was swinging open. Barry's heart raced.

He saw the figure in the doorway; big, fat, covered in red silky clothes. The light from the street outside came through the window silhouetting him. Barry saw the huge grey bag on his shoulder, he heard the clinks and knocks of many things inside the bag. Barry's heart raced. He knew he was going to attempt something no child had attempted before. He wanted the whole bag of toys.

As Santa stepped forward and bent over the paper bag at the foot of the bed, Barry reached over the side of the bed, down to the floor. He gripped his grandfather's mighty walking stick and brought it up with a grunt. He barely made out Santa's head, and he aimed and let fly. Whang! The bag flew from Santa's shoulder. Santa clapped his hands to his head and tumbled on the floor.

Barry sprang from the bed. He was halfway out of the room with Santa's bag on his shoulder when he heard his grandfather's voice: 'Lord have mercy, uh dead, uh dead!'

Inside the story

In groups

1 Talk about how you see Barry; the sort of boy he is and the life he leads. There are quite a few clues in the story.

2 How do you see Barry's grandfather?

3 How do you feel about what happens to the Grandfather? Is it funny? shocking? fair? unfair? . . . something else?

4 When you were younger, did you believe in Santa Claus or the Tooth Fairy, or some other mysterious and magical person who would bring you gifts, provided you behaved in what adults considered to be the right way? Did any of you ever try to stay awake to see Santa Claus? Share your memories about what it was like, what things happened and how you felt. If you have a strong memory of a particular occasion, tell the story to the rest of the group.

On your own

Imagine what Barry and his Grandfather say to each other when they realise what has happened. Try to see the situation from both points of view and write the exchange.

ZELDA

Emily Rodda

Her name was Zelda. That was the first thing about her. Let's face it, it's not the most ordinary name in the world, is it? I know lots of kids have unusual names. But it doesn't seem to matter with them. I mean, you wouldn't say Blaise, or Makela, or Sion were ordinary names. It was just that Zelda didn't . . . just didn't suit her name. Or maybe she did. She was as odd as it was. Maybe that was the trouble. Blaise and Sion and Makela – they were just like everyone else. But Zelda was different.

If I said that to Mum she'd say, 'What do you mean, "different"?' And I'd say something like, 'Well, she has this long hair that she wears in a bun. Black hair. In a bun. With a hairnet over it. And she's got a very fat face, and white skin that looks sort of thick. And her nails are really long and cut into these points, you know, like Auntie Meg's.'

And Mum'd say, in that irritating, reasonable way she has, 'People don't all have to look alike, you know, Jess. You never used to be so conservative.'

'It's not just what she looks like, Mum,' I'd say. 'It's what she's like. It's . . .' And then I'd give up, because I couldn't really say what it was that made Zelda odd kid out. But that's what she was. From our first day in Year Seven, that's what she was.

We were all from different schools. All girls. Some people had friends who'd come up from primary with them. Most didn't. But after the first few days most of us had found someone to have lunch with, or talk to in class, or whatever. But that was when I noticed Zelda. She was always by herself. She'd get to school alone, go from class to class by herself, sit alone, reading or just staring into space, at lunch-time. And, you know, it wasn't as if she was actually shy, I don't think. Or not in the usual way, anyway. Shy kids take longer than the others to, you know, get warmed up, and link up with a group, but you can tell they feel shy and want to, and you know that eventually they'll get talking with someone or other and that'll get them started. Harriet, one of my friends, was like that.

But with Zelda you didn't get that feeling. You didn't get any feeling about her at all, really. It was like she was a little drop of oil paint and all the rest of us were drops of water, in a glass. She was just separate, and different, and you just wouldn't know what she was feeling or thinking about.

Somehow you couldn't imagine Zelda having parents, or a house, or anything like that. Well, you could imagine her having them, I suppose, but you couldn't imagine what her parents would be like, or how she'd talk to them. I could imagine her sitting in her bedroom, though. Sitting at a desk in front of a window, I used to think, with her homework in front of her. She'd be looking out the window, her big, white face quite still, like it used to look mostly in class, or in the playground, and you wouldn't know what she was thinking about.

Well, anyway, after a few weeks had gone by and everyone was getting really settled down and confident, the class had sort of divided naturally into groups. You know how it happens. And one of these groups had a couple of kids in it I really didn't like. Their names were Berwyn and Michelle. To be honest, it wasn't quite that I didn't like them, I suppose. It was that I was scared of them. I suppose that sounds stupid.

I don't mean they were scary like they'd hit you on the head with a brick and run off with your lunch money, or that sort of thing. They were scary to me because they were really, sort of, glamorous – you know? They were really good looking, for a start, and they looked older and trendier than anyone else. And they knew things. They knew how things were done. I mean, on day one at high school we all turned up with shiny black clodhopper shoes, and skirts down to our knees and white school shirts from Grace Brothers, and everything. And somehow or other they'd known in advance they'd get away with black canvas shoes and big white T-shirts from the markets, and school skirts hitched half-way up their thighs, and they'd come along looking really smooth. I mean, even if I'd known about how to make the uniform look trendy, Mum wouldn't have let me do it. Not on the first day. Not in a fit.

And Berwyn and Michelle, Berwyn especially, never did anything stupid, or embarrassing. They were never, like, too serious about anything, either. If you're too serious about things, or try too hard at things, it leaves you, sort of, open, you know? You can end up looking like an idiot. People can laugh at you, and send you up. Berwyn and Michelle knew that. I think they must have known it since kindergarten, they were so good at being cool.

The thing was, they despised anyone who wasn't like them. And that was what scared me. I would've liked to be like them, but I knew I wasn't, and I couldn't make myself not care about what they thought of me. I was scared of their superior little smiles, and the way they didn't feel they had to be friendly, or even polite, to other people, and the sarcastic things they said when someone irritated them and the way they whispered to one another, laughing behind their hands, and looking at you.

That was Berwyn and Michelle. The rest of the group weren't quite so cool. There were some gigglers among them, and others of them you could talk to okay, when they were by themselves. When they were by themselves they were quite nice, really. But when they were with Berwyn and Michelle they whispered behind their hands and tittered and said smart, cool things to each other, and flicked their hair back, and stared at you as if you were weird, or your nose was snotty or something.

Well, this day I'm talking about we had a double English period before lunch. Our English teacher that year was Mrs Stephenson, who was also our class teacher. She was nice, and didn't yell or anything, and she was very keen on creative writing. I liked that, so I looked forward to English, usually. Since the beginning of term she'd been getting us to write descriptions of a place, a person, an animal, and so on. This day she said she wanted us to spend the second period writing a description of ourselves – not in the first person, but as though someone else was writing it. She said it was a rather difficult exercise, but she wanted us to try it.

Some kids groaned, and I saw Berwyn and Michelle look at each other and raise their eyebrows in that bored way they had, but no one mucked up on Mrs Stephenson, so eventually we all settled down and started writing. She was right. It's much harder than you'd think, writing about yourself – what you look like and everything. It makes you feel embarrassed. I mean, I think I look quite good, but I didn't want Mrs Stephenson to think I was conceited or anything. And then I couldn't really remember what I did look like, somehow – which sounds ridiculous, but I mean, you just try it! It's really hard, no matter how many times you've looked in a mirror. Anyway, somehow I filled up a page, and I guess it was okay. But I could hardly stand to read over what I'd written. It was really, sort of, personal and embarrassing.

Mrs Stephenson usually collected any writing we'd done at the end of the period, but this time she said she'd like us to read over what we'd written for homework, and make any changes we thought might improve it. She said she'd collect our papers after roll-call the next day. I stuffed my essay into my folder and went out with everyone else for lunch. It was Geography with Mrs Fox in the same room after.

At lunch everyone was talking about the exercise. Some people said it was boring. Other people, like me, said it was really hard. Berwyn and Michelle and that group said it was pointless, and typical of Mrs Stephenson, who was a complete dag and wore hopeless clothes – and they started making up a description of her, all about her varicose veins and support stockings and permed hair. I don't know what Zelda thought about the essay, because as usual she was sitting by herself right away from the crowd, eating her sandwiches. She wasn't reading that day, just staring into space, chewing, chewing, chewing.

I saw Berwyn look at Zelda and nudge Michelle. She whispered something and Michelle grinned. They walked over to the rubbish bin near where Zelda was sitting and tossed in their papers. Then Michelle started to make these moo-ing noises.

Berwyn was killing herself laughing and all the other kids in their group, plus quite a few of the others, started giggling too. But Zelda didn't turn her head. Maybe she didn't hear. Maybe she didn't know the noises were aimed at her. Maybe she did, and didn't care. You couldn't tell with Zelda.

Berwyn and Michelle walked back to their gang and got a hero's welcome. They all went off in a huddle, and every now and then for the rest of lunchtime you'd hear a loud moo, and a chorus of giggles, from their spot under the pepper tree. I thought it was pretty pathetic, actually, and so did some of my friends. Mean, too, even though Zelda didn't seem to know what was going on, or care.

It was quite a hot day, that day, and I remember feeling really slow and heavy when Harriet and I walked back into the classroom after lunch. It has been so bright outside that everything looked dim, although the lights were on. We hadn't hurried, and there were already quite a few kids in the room. I remember really clearly seeing Berwyn and Michelle and some of the others standing in a little group round one of the desks. Berwyn was reading something aloud, and the others were collapsing with laughter. One of them, Sylvia, turned and looked round as Harriet and I came in. Her face was bright pink, and tears were actually streaming down her face, she was laughing so much.

They were at Zelda's desk, reading her description of herself. Berwyn had the paper in her hand.

Suddenly I felt myself blushing red, blushing really badly, so my cheeks burned. My whole stomach seemed to turn over, and I felt sick.

I can't explain to you how awful the feeling was. Or why it was so awful. Or why, when I realised Zelda wasn't in the room, hadn't come in yet, I acted the way I did. I mean, I didn't even know Zelda, or like her, or anything. But suddenly it seemed to me as though I was watching someone absolutely helpless being, sort of, invaded by something not human. Suddenly it was like Zelda wasn't the odd kid out at all, but part of me, and Harriet, and all the other people in the world who weren't cool, and cruel, and fearless.

So I went up to Berwyn, who I'd hardly even spoken to before, and took the paper out of her hand. I said, 'That's not yours,' and I put the paper behind my back.

She looked surprised, really surprised, and then she smiled really sarcastically and shook her head and said, 'Jessica, you're red as a beetroot.'

But Michelle said, 'Who do you think you are, Jessie Simons. Give that back!' And she made a grab for the paper.

I wouldn't give it up, though, and I pushed past them and shoved the essay back in Zelda's folder and stood there, sweating and blushing, with my heart beating furiously, and after a while they all melted back to their own places, because they could hear Mrs Fox and the rest of the class coming down the corridor.

So I went back to my desk too, and sat down. My knees were trembling and I could feel my shirt soaking wet on my back and under my arms. I didn't look at anyone, not at Harriet or anyone. Zelda came in with the others and sat down, and though a few people giggled no one said or did anything – to me or to her.

Zelda sat at her desk, and looked at Mrs Fox, waiting for her to start the lesson. She didn't know what had happened. She didn't have any idea that she'd been invaded. She was as separate from me and the rest of us as ever, with her small blank eyes, and her pointy fingernails. She didn't know that for

a moment we'd been sisters, and faced an enemy together.

The next morning Mrs Stephenson collected our descriptions, and a few days later we got them back. I got an A for mine, and she put 'Some nice touches, Jessica' on the bottom. I sometimes wonder what Zelda got. I saw a few sentences of it, when I put it back in the folder. Zelda had written, with very curly loops, in fine black pen: 'She has lustrous black hair that falls in a rich cascade to her waist. Her hair is hardly ever cut, only to take off split ends. She wears shoes with heels about four centimetres high . . .'

Zelda left our school the next year, and I don't know where she went after that. For some reason I often think about her, and wonder what happened to her. Berwyn and Michelle and the others haven't ever forgotten what I did that day, I don't think. Well, I guess they have in one way – they wouldn't, probably, give someone like me a second thought, once the first excitement was over. But I suppose what I mean is that where some of the kids I go round with are invited to their parties, and things like that, I never am. I think that day they wrote me off for ever as uncool, and a goody-goody, and maybe a bit mad, and that was that, even though now they've forgotten the thing that started it all.

I have my own friends, though, and I don't care about Berwyn and Michelle. And I'm not scared of them any more, either. I haven't been, since that day.

It seems to me that growing up is a bit like waking up, bit by bit. You go along, dreaming, thinking you're awake and that you understand how things are, and you're seeing things clearly. And then something happens, or you read something, or someone says something to you, and you blink, and suddenly the world's more in focus than it was before, and you realise you haven't been properly awake at all.

Probably that's why I remember Zelda, and that day. That day was one of my 'waking up' times. I understood a few more things after that.

Not that I understood about Zelda. She was as much a mystery to me after that day as she ever was – well, more, in fact. But somehow I got a bit more of the picture about the world, and how I fitted into it. What side I was on, in fact.

Do you know what I mean?

Inside the story

In pairs or groups

1 When Jess's mum tries to get her to say what it is about Zelda that made her 'the odd kid out', she can't really explain. What do you think Jess might have said if she had made a real effort to put her feelings into words?

2 Discuss how Jess feels about Berwyn and Michelle at the beginning of the story, and what effect they have on her and on the other pupils.

3 Jess says that she didn't even know Zelda or like her particularly, so why did she snatch the paper from Berwyn?

4 The incident over Zelda's work is a turning-point for Jess in the way she sees both herself and others, and she leaves us with a question right at the end of the story: 'Do you know what I mean?' Talk about what *you* think Jess means when she says, 'But somehow I got a bit more of the picture about the world, and how I fitted into it. What side I was on, in fact.'

On your own

1 Try Mrs Stephenson's exercise and write a description of yourself in the third person – as though someone else was writing it. Is it as difficult to do as Jess says it is? If so, what makes it difficult?

2 Write a description of what happened with Zelda's paper from the point of view of Berwyn or Michelle. You will have to think yourself into their characters and find the right tone of voice.

3 Write your own story based on an incident where someone at school is treated meanly or unfairly, or is bullied in some way. Try to get inside the minds of the people involved and to explore what it is they – those meting out the treatment, whoever is on the receiving end, those watching – are feeling.

THE TROUT
Sean O'Faolain

One of the first places Julia always ran to when they arrived in G— was The Dark Walk. It is a laurel walk, very old; almost gone wild; a lofty midnight tunnel of smooth, sinewy branches. Underfoot the tough brown leaves are never dry enough to crackle: there is always a suggestion of damp and cool trickle.

She raced right into it. For the first few yards she always had the memory of the sun behind her, then she felt the dusk closing swiftly down on her so that she screamed with pleasure and raced on to reach the light at the far end; and it was always just a little too long in coming so that she emerged gasping, clasping her hands, laughing, drinking in the sun. When she was filled with the heat and glare she would turn and consider the ordeal again.

This year she had the extra joy of showing it to her small brother, and of terrifying him as well as herself. And for him the fear lasted longer because his legs were so short and she had gone out at the far end while he was still screaming and racing.

When they had done this many times they came back to the house to tell everybody that they had done it. He boasted. She mocked. They squabbled.

'Cry babby!'

'You were afraid yourself, so there!'

'I won't take you any more.'

'You're a big pig.'

'I hate you.'

Tears were threatening, so somebody said, 'Did you see the well?' She opened her eyes at that and held up her long lovely neck suspiciously and decided to be incredulous. She was twelve and at that age little girls are beginning to suspect most stories: they have already found out too many, from Santa Claus to the stork. How could there be a well! In the Dark Walk? That she had visited year after year? Haughtily she said, 'Nonsense.'

But she went back, pretending to be going somewhere else, and she found a hole scooped in the rock at the side of the walk, choked with damp leaves, so shrouded by ferns that she uncovered it only after much searching. At the back of this little cavern there was about a quart of water. In the water she suddenly perceived a panting trout. She rushed for Stephen and dragged him to see, and they were both so excited that they were no longer afraid of the darkness as they hunched down and peered in at the fish panting in his tiny prison, his silver stomach going up and down like an engine.

Nobody knew how the trout got there. Even old Martin in the kitchen garden laughed and refused to believe that it was there, or pretended not to believe, until she forced him to come down and see. Kneeling and pushing back his tattered old cap he peered in.

'Be cripes, you're right. How the divil in hell did that fella get there?'

She stared at him suspiciously.

'You knew?' she accused; but he said, 'The divil a' know,' and reached down to lift it out. Convinced, she hauled him back. If she had found it, then it was her trout.

Her mother suggested that a bird had carried the spawn. Her father thought that in the winter a small streamlet might have carried it down there as a baby, and it had been safe until the summer came and the water began to dry up. She said, 'I see,' and went back to look again and consider the matter in private. Her brother remained behind, wanting to hear the whole story of the trout, not really interested in the actual trout but much more interested in the story which his mummy began to make up for him on the lines of, 'So one day Daddy Trout and Mammy Trout . . .' When he related it to her she said, 'Pooh.'

It troubled her that the trout was always in the same position; he had no room to turn; all the time the silver belly went up and down; otherwise he was motionless. She wondered what he ate, and in between visits to Joey Pony and the boat, and a bathe to get cool, she thought of his hunger. She brought him down bits of dough; once she brought him a worm. He ignored the food. He just went on panting. Hunched over him she thought how all the winter, while she was at school, he had been in there. All the winter, in The Dark Walk, all day, all night, floating around alone. She drew the leaf of her hat down around her ears and chin and stared. She was still thinking of it as she lay in bed.

It was late June, the longest days of the year. The sun had sat still for a week, burning up the world. Although it was after ten o'clock it was still bright and still hot. She lay on her back under a single sheet, with her long legs spread, trying to keep cool. She could see the D of the moon through the fir tree – they slept on the ground floor. Before they went to bed her mummy had told Stephen the story of the

trout again, and she, in her bed, had resolutely presented her back to them and read her book. But she had kept one ear cocked.

'And so, in the end, this naughty fish who would not stay at home got bigger and bigger and bigger, and the water got smaller and smaller . . .'

Passionately she had whirled and cried, 'Mummy, don't make it a horrible old moral story!' Her mummy had brought in a fairy godmother then, who sent lots of rain, and filled the well, and a stream poured out and the trout floated away down to the river below. Staring at the moon she knew that there are no such things as fairy godmothers and that the trout, down in The Dark Walk, was panting like an engine. She heard somebody unwind a fishing reel. Would the *beasts* fish him out!

She sat up. Stephen was a hot lump of sleep, lazy thing. The Dark Walk would be full of little scraps of moon. She leaped up and looked out the window, and somehow it was not so lightsome now that she saw the dim mountains far away and the black firs against the breathing land and heard a dog say *bark-bark*. Quietly she lifted the ewer of water and climbed out the window and scuttled along the cool but cruel gravel down to the maw of the tunnel. Her pyjamas were very short so that when she splashed water it wet her ankles. She peered into the tunnel. Something alive rustled inside there. She raced in, and up and down she raced, and flurried, and cried aloud, 'Oh, gosh, I can't find it,' and then at last she did. Kneeling down in the damp she put her hand into the slimy hole. When the body lashed they were both mad with fright. But she gripped him and shoved him into the ewer and raced, with her teeth ground, out to the other end of the tunnel and down the steep paths to the river's edge.

All the time she could feel him lashing his tail

against the side of the ewer. She was afraid he would jump right out. The gravel cut into her soles until she came to the cool ooze of the river's bank where the moon mice on the water crept into her feet. She poured out, watching until he plopped. For a second he was visible in the water. She hoped he was not dizzy. Then all she saw was the glimmer of the moon in the silent-flowing river, the dark firs, the dim mountains, and the radiant pointed face laughing down at her out of the empty sky.

She scuttled up the hill, in the window, plonked down the ewer, and flew through the air like a bird into bed. The dog said *bark-bark*. She heard the fishing reel whirring. She hugged herself and giggled. Like a river of joy her holiday spread before her.

In the morning Stephen rushed to her, shouting that 'he' was gone, and asking 'where' and 'how'. Lifting her nose in the air she said superciliously, 'Fairy godmother, I suppose?' and strolled away patting the palms of her hands.

Inside the story

In pairs

1 Talk about why Julia feels as she does about the trout and why you think she finally has to do something to free the creature.

2 When she has released the trout into the river, Julia seems almost to feel release and happiness herself. Why do you think this is?

On your own

1 Reread the opening two or three paragraphs of the story. The Dark Walk is a favourite place of Julia's and she enjoys the sense of fear she experiences when she runs down it. Think of any place that is a favourite with you: it could be somewhere you feel completely happy, or, like The Dark Walk for Julia, it could be a place that you enjoy because it is a bit creepy. Try to capture the atmosphere of the place in two or three paragraphs of descriptive writing. Can you explain how you feel when you are there?

2 Julia's feelings are quite complicated. Try to capture them in a letter that she writes to a friend back home in which she describes what happened and how she felt about the attitudes of the other people – her little brother, her mother and father, and old Martin.

THE RAINBOW CLOCK
Susan Gregory

'Dear Delroy,' wrote Surinder. 'How are you? I hope you are doing well in school.'

Surinder stared in front of him at the objects on his desk top. His dad had bought him the desk only this year, so that he could study in his bedroom. That's what he ought to be doing, studying, not struggling with a letter to blooming Delroy. Surinder began to arrange his biros and pencils in a neat line along the desk top, and straightened every book and every piece of paper. Then he took the pencils out of the straight line and sharpened every one. With a sigh he returned at last to the letter. He read through what he had written five times, and stared in front of him again.

Surinder hated writing letters. He hated it at any time, but tonight there were so many other things he ought to be doing. There was his Biology homework for a start. Then he wanted to revise Chemistry for half an hour and work on some Physics problems for another half and then read the paper for fifteen minutes (so important to keep up with World Events). He looked in despair at the three pages of closely packed writing that his friend from Birmingham had sent and he sighed. Hadn't Delroy anything better to do these days? When they'd lived next door to one another before Surinder had moved to Leicester, they used to spend every evening together, studying. They'd done projects together. They'd tested one another when it came to exams. They'd built kits together when Surinder's timetable said 'Half an Hour's Necessary Relaxation Time.' Delroy had even copied Surinder's timetable, so that when it was 9.55 pm, 'Time for a Relaxing Drink and Fifteen Minutes with Newspaper And/Or First Half of *News at Ten*', Surinder knew that next door Delroy would know it was time for exactly the same thing.

Now Delroy had time on his hands, it seemed, to squander writing a whole lot of rubbish about *girls*! Surinder snorted.

He got up and drew his bedroom curtains together so that they lined up exactly and sat down again and took up his pen. He was the only person he knew to use proper ink and a fountain pen, just like his father had before him. He carefully drew a hair out of the nib and wiped his fingers on a tissue from the box he had covered with computer paper and labelled TISSUES in bold black ink. He was proud of that touch. 'Something a little bit *different*,' he had said to Delroy when he came to stay. Delroy had thought his room was great. Everything in it was black and white – black and white graph-paper curtains, a white Anglepoise lamp on his black fibreglass desk, filing cabinet white with black handles, black and white chess set cover on his bed, black and white digital clock on the white table by the bedside. Only the carpet was beige – white would have got filthy, black would have shown up the bits. Surinder hated bits. There were no unnecessary objects on Surinder's shiny surfaces, no pictures on his gleaming white walls. 'Wish my dad had the bread to let me kit out my room like this,' Delroy had said to Surinder, running his brown hands with their pale pink nails admiringly over the lacquered veneers, clean as an operating theatre. He eyed again the tissue box neatly backed with computer paper and labelled TISSUES in bold black ink.

But the fact that Delroy might even now also be drawing a white tissue from a tissue box wrapped in computer paper and labelled TISSUES in bold black ink was no comfort to Surinder. Delroy was a dead loss these days, a waste of precious time.

'I am sorry I couldn't write this letter earlier on, as I am revising for the Christmas exams.' Surinder stuck his tongue down his pen top and whistled dolefully, pulling at his turban. He'd never be done at this rate. One sentence every five minutes. Surinder thought again.

'Will you write me at the most once a month, not once a week, as it is more economical.' Surinder looked at his watch: 7.41. His timetable said, '7.55: *If time*, go downstairs for Reviving Cup of Coffee'. There was no way he could take fifteen minutes just getting down the stairs. Perhaps he could squeeze in fifteen minutes of *The Times* and catching up with World Events? Or fifteen minutes 'Exercising Time: A Healthy Mind in a Healthy Body'? No, he'd only have twelve minutes and forty-three seconds at it now. Surinder shuddered. That wouldn't do at all. But twelve minutes and thirty-odd seconds struggling to write to his friend!

'I always find it hard to write letters as I don't know what to say. If English was my best subject, not my worst, I would find it easy. As you know, my best subject is Physics, next is Chemistry.' Inspiration at last! 'Talking about writing, you remember that white fellow Robert Russell (Rusty) you met when you were here? His ambition is to be "aerodynamic engineer" yet he dosen't do any homework. For instance, Afzal was away for a week and I borrowed him all my school books so he could catch up. It took him just one night to catch everything up. Some time ago Robert missed 3½ days off school and he still hasn't caught up with the average pupils despite me and Afzal borrowing him our books *many times*.'

Surinder, encouraged by this flood, thought again.

'You remember that fellow Salim I used to write you about? Well I do not hang around with Salim so much now as he is usually absent.

'With best wishes.

   Your sincerely,

    Surinder Singh (Mr)

     146 Upton Street,

      Leicester,

       LE2 4PG

        Great Britain,

         United Kingdom,

          The Free World.'

'PS Tommorow is our first EXAM.'

Surinder looked at his watch. He leapt up, folded the paper so that the two edges met precisely, slid it into the envelope, flicked with his tongue to the right, to the left, and stuck the letter down with a bang of the fist. He took the stairs two at a time and made it to the kettle just as the digital clock flickered to 7.55 . . .

It was a week later and Surinder was struggling with composition again. In his English lesson this time. The exams were over, and they were back to routine with double English. Bor-ing.

They'd just done Duncan being murdered by Macbeth. 'I want you to make up your own newspaper,' said Mr Melbourne. 'The main story will be the murder of Duncan. Splash headlines. King slain at Thane of Cawdor's castle. You know the kind of thing. Exclusive interview with Lady Macbeth. Report on the foulness of the night. Feature on local superstitions – horses eating one another. That sort of thing. Then anything you like to make it lively – puzzles, adverts, sports reports, cartoons, special interest stories. Just use your imagination.'

Surinder groaned. A whole double period to be filled with all that *writing*! 'Anything you like,' he said. 'Just use your imagination,' he said. Well, Surinder simply hadn't *got* an imagination. And that was that.

When the bell rang at the end of the first lesson, Surinder had written at the top of his large sheet of paper, 'The Scottish Times.' Underneath he had written, 'King Slain at Thane of Cawdor's Castle'. Underneath *that* he had written, 'The king was slain last night at the Thane of Cawdor's castle. There is an exclusive interview with Lady Macbeth on page two. The weather was fowl. The horses ate one another. Inside you will find puzzles, adverts, sports reports and special interest stories.'

After that he'd been pulling at his turban and getting ink on his tongue from sticking it down his pen top and making very discreet popping noises. Surinder looked around at what the other kids were doing. Afzal was staring out of the window. Very, very occasionally he'd made a mark on a piece of paper. He was counting how many BMWs went past the school in a week. Afzal meant to own a BMW by the time he was thirty. If too many went past, though, he'd change it to a Lotus Élite.

David March was staring at the ceiling where a spider promenaded round and round the rim of the light just above his desk. Every now and then the spider would burn its feet and spin a hasty web. But it always climbed up to the same light bowl again. Surinder sighed.

Wasn't *anybody* working properly? Surinder's eye fell on Topaz Smith. She had her head down and was scribbling frantically with a pale pink plastic ballpoint shaped to look like a quill pen. Every now and then her shoulders would heave up and down.

Topaz Smith was a weirdo. She was always in trouble for her multi-coloured patchwork jackets, her floating scarves and her dingle-dangle earrings. She had a spiky red fringe and a streaky ponytail growing out of one ear and went on and on in Discussion. Topaz Smith did not know her place and Surinder couldn't stand her.

Topaz dashed down the quill pen and snatched up a pencil. (She did everything in fits and starts.) She examined the end of it with a grand gesture, flung her fingers against the spiked fringe and groaned. Then she tore across to the waste-paper basket where she was soon joking with Candy Atkinson. Sir let them talk while they worked if they wanted to, which Surinder thought a grave mistake.

Cautiously Surinder left his desk and bent over Topaz's paper to see what all the scribbling was about.

Topaz had called her newspaper 'The Daily Rain'. She had drawn a huge puddle in the top lefthand corner with a giant raindrop plopping into it. 'Read "The Daily Rain",' it said, 'for the best in Splash Headlines.' Surinder snorted. Trust it to be silly! The front page was dominated by a single word picked out in vivid tartan. 'MACDEATH!' it read. 'By your raving reporter Jock Strapp.' The report began: 'It was Macduff who first beheld the gherrizzly, gherrastly, gherrimish sight. "There was only one word for it," Macduff was quoted as saying, "MACabre." ' Surinder snorted again, quickly scanning the headlines of the other news items:

HAGGIS WORKERS SAY 'NO' TO SOYA BEAN

LEYLAND CARTS GO ON STRIKE

STUPID BOY TO LIVE ON PIG FARM

And the advertisements:

'Bill's kilts: With sporran. Complete satisfaction guaranteed
Send large carrier pigeon to . . .'
'Coffinmate. Coffee for Vampires.'
'Protect your sporran from MOTH.'
'Personal. Small dog requires large cat for *chasing round garden and* GENUINE FRIENDSHIP.'

Surinder looked at the Special Features. 'Exclusive interview with Society Hostess, Lady "Chi Chi" Macbeth. Page Three.' Surinder turned over the page. A cut-out picture of Joan Collins, showing a lot of cleavage and raising a Martini glass, winked up at him. Surinder closed his eyes. When he opened them again his attention was caught by something in the Sports Report.

SEMI-FINAL OF SPLENDID MACJOUST
Sir Hamish versus Sir Beamish.
Sir Angus versus Surinder.
Favourite to Win: Surinder Singer Sewing Machine.
Six to Four On.

Surinder's mouth twitched at the same time as his eyebrows knitted. For his name was entirely surrounded with hearts! He turned over the page and caught his breath again. For there was a huge picture of a very large turban, a maroon turban, *his* turban, upside down with a load of rubbish spewing out of it. And across it, so there could be no doubt, Topaz had scrawled 'TUR-BIN'. Underneath she had written, 'Top Quality Refuse Depository: SURIN'S TUR-BINS'. In spite of the insult, though, the SURIN was still surrounded by hearts!

At that moment Topaz bounded back. Surinder quickly flapped the page over.

'What you doing round my desk, Surinder?' demanded Topaz. There was a hopeful look in her eyes.

Surinder was caught off his guard. He couldn't tackle her there and then about the dread insult she'd paid him. Besides, he recalled Surinder, Favourite to Win, and the hearts, and he didn't know quite what to think!

'I . . . I wondered if I could look at your Macbeth book,' Surinder said feebly, 'to get some ideas.' Topaz had her own copy of the play, new out. Her mum had brought it back for her, a present from London. Sir had shown them all. It was the real play but all done in cartoons. Sir thought it was great, Surinder that it was daft.

'Forgot it today,' said Topaz, crossing her fingers and edging her bag out of sight with her toe. 'But you can come round my house after school and borrow it, Surinder. Stay to tea if you like.'

Surinder could not believe his ears. Go to a *girl's* house? She had to be out of her mind. 'S'all right,' he said. 'Got too much work to do. Haven't the time.'

'I'll bring it round your house after tea then,' said Topaz straight off, looking at him with the bright eyes of a spider who has just netted a particularly dense fly. With a heavy heart Surinder settled back down to attempt another headline story. 'HAGGIS WORKERS SAY "NO"~TO SOYA BEAN . . .'

So quarter to four witnessed the unlikely sight of Surinder Singh walking home with Topaz Smith. 'Can't stop,' muttered Surinder, eyes dodging this way and that. 'Haven't the time. I'll just pick the book up, then go.'

Topaz looked at him. She scrabbled in her peacock-tail-shaped shoulder bag and drew out a cartoon she'd done. It showed an alarm clock with a long grey beard, wearing a crown and a kilt, with a dagger up its nose and sitting in a puddle of blood. Underneath it said, 'Macbeth hath murdered Time.' She handed it to him. 'There you are, Surinder,' she said. 'Time's dead. You needn't worry about Time any longer.' Surinder looked at it and looked at her. He was at a complete loss. 'It's *sleep*,' he said scornfully at last. 'Macbeth hath murdered *sleep*.' Topaz stared at him. Then with a shake of her head and a heave of her shoulders she pulled out her plastic quill, took the cartoon from him, stopped at a wall, leant the paper on it and drew the alarm clock, some closed eyes and a lot of trailing ZZZZZZZZZZZZZZZs coming out of his bloody nose, and changed *Time* to *Sleep*. She put the pen and the cartoon away and bounded very close to Surinder. 'You're a slave to your brain, you know that, Sewing Machine?' she said affectionately, jogging up against his elbow. 'And *nearly* as boring as Afzal.'

Topaz stopped by the front gate of a terraced house in Norland Street. To say it was a terraced house doesn't make it sound very exciting. Surinder lived in a terraced house very similar to this one. That is to say, the same structure, the same stone scrolls on either side of the door, the same mangy-looking privet hedge round the tiny paved front garden. But whereas Surinder's house was a discreet fume-blackened stone with discreet smut-ingrained stone scrolls, and discreetly painted with the dark green paint that had become regulation for that block, Topaz's house was more like a child's idea of a house, entirely constructed of sweets. The front door was barley-sugar gold; the left-hand downstairs window frames were a lollipop red and the right a peppermint green, while upstairs they were sherbet lemon and blackcurrant purple; the entire facing wall was painted milk chocolate, with one scroll the jewel colours of wine-gums, and the other, sugar-almond shades – soft pink, peach and the palest of aquamarines. Topaz's house looked good enough to eat.

Except you didn't eat houses. Houses, like schools, meant good solid achievement, the sound investment of time. Surinder sniffed.

Topaz opened the door. It wasn't locked. Instead of going into a dark narrow hall with the stairs leading steeply out, you stepped into a big room with the stairs going out of one corner. The Smiths had knocked down a wall. You could tell they had knocked it down because they had left bits of it lying untidily about.

The room was like a puppet theatre hit by the blitz. The walls that still stood were painted a fiery orange, the wall up the stairs was purple and the floorboards were red – no carpet, except on the walls. At least Surinder had the impression that the walls were a fiery orange or a deep purple but it was difficult to tell because everything was so sprinkled over with *things*. Suns and moons and planets and parrots and seagulls and pierrots-on-stars and babies-on-clouds dangled and spun before the eyes all around the stairs area, and in the main room were shawls and feathers and velvet and net and a black lace fan half-closed like a butterfly's wings, cables of sequins and beads, and posters and hanging plants and plaited string and jangling shells and bells. A moose's head with a sparkly necklace round it jutted out of the wall and the room smelt of moth-balls and wood smoke, marmalade, cinnamon and pine. In the middle of the floor was a grand piano. It was painted green where it wasn't all over flowers and ferns and fabulous beasts. There was no other furniture – just large cushions – and a great many books. No bookcases. They simply spilt and toppled about.

Topaz told Surinder to sit down and clattered off up the stairs screeching 'Mum!' The kitchen door opened and a little girl came out.

She looked like a child from a nursery rhyme with her blonde hair cut square round the cheeks and her full deep fringe. She was dressed in an all-in-one striped suit like a clown's with big red pom-poms down the front. She came over to Surinder and stood in front of him, staring. At last she said, 'Why you got a tea-cosy on your head?'

She didn't wait for a reply. 'I'm making up songs about carrots this week,' she told him. 'Do you want "Carrots Go on a Picnic" or "Carrots Cleaning Their Teeth"?'

Surinder opened his mouth. There was a colossal stampeding on the stairs and Topaz's legs appeared, followed by the bottom half of what turned out to be a large woman in a dragon-covered dressing-gown with a bandage of plaited scarves round her head.

'Surinder!' she said, holding out her hand. 'Hullo there. You've met William, I see. Take Surinder into the kitchen, Topaz, and let him find himself something to eat.'

Surinder was so astonished to discover the clown suit housed a *boy* that he'd followed Topaz into the kitchen before he'd had a chance to mumble that he hadn't the time. Surinder was glad he'd been told beforehand that the room he'd just entered was the kitchen because everything was dressed up to look like something else. The cooker looked like the Space Control Center at Houston, the table was a toadstool, the stools were mushrooms, and rose-coloured clouds floated past the window across a clear blue sky, though Surinder distinctly remembered it had started to rain. Topaz flung open a fridge door that had been painted all over with spiders complete with their webs. 'What would you like?' she asked, and Surinder peered in. He swallowed and thought desperately, deciding they couldn't interfere too much with a bottle of milk. What price a tissue box covered with computer paper and labelled TISSUES in bold black ink after *this*?

'Just a glass of milk, please,' said Surinder weakly. Topaz pulled a face but she handed him the bottle and a ruby red plastic drinking mug with a yellow plastic straw snaking out of it. He noticed she poured milk for herself in an *ordinary* glass, but to this she immediately added a dash of blackcurrant juice and stirred it all up with a spoon disguised as a spanner. She carved herself bread from a hefty-looking loaf and piled on a lot of purply pink salami. She held it

up against the contents of the glass and nodded. 'I do so like my food to *tone*,' she explained to a mystified Surinder, taking a gulp of the violet-coloured milk.

As Topaz gulped, a multi-hued bird with wings like a feather boa flung itself out of a clock with a Kermit the Frog face and an upside-down rainbow for a mouth. It eeyored twice to mark the half-hour and Surinder's timetable flapped straight out of the rose-tinted window as he beheld Topaz's lilac moustache and the tawny ponytail springing out of one ear. And his heart jerked and boinged in time to the grand piano which at that moment struck up an improvised tune to 'Carrots Cleaning Their Teeth'. For Surinder Sewing Machine Singh and Topaz Matilda-Jane Smith, time simply stood still.

That night Surinder's father yelled up the stairs to say that they were five, eight, twelve, *fifteen* minutes into *News at Ten* and Surinder's Relaxing Drink had developed a skin. Surinder, however, was busy explaining to Delroy that he wasn't going to be a brain surgeon after all but would be owning a whole chain of jewellers' shops instead. In each of his stores he would be dedicating an entire window to displaying a single gem and in every one there would be a scroll curling out of a broken alarm clock, emblazoned with the device 'A Topaz is For Ever . . .'. His father hollered up the stairs for absolutely the last time to recall to his son's mind the grave importance of keeping up with World Events. But Surinder didn't even hear him as he started his fourth closely packed page to his Birmingham friend . . .

Inside the story

In pairs or groups

1 Discuss Surinder's character in the first part of the story, up to the point where he finishes his letter. Think about how he behaves; what he likes and why; what matters most to him. Make a list of words that you think describe him up to this point.

Now talk about Topaz in the same way. Think about how she behaves in school and on the way home. Make another list of words that you think describe *her*.

2 Is it just chance that Surinder ends up back at Topaz's house? Why do you think so?

3 Discuss why the Smith household is such a shock to Surinder.

4 The title of the story – 'The Rainbow Clock' – suggests that both *time* and *colour* are important ideas in the story. See how many references to each of these you can find in the story: you will probably find most at the beginning and at the end.

5 How have Surinder's ideas (particularly about time and colour) changed by the end of the story?

On your own

1 The story ends with Surinder writing a long letter to his friend in Birmingham. Write the letter you imagine he might have sent to Delroy about the day's happenings. You could include what happened at school and how he felt; what happened on the way home; how he felt about the Smiths' house and how he felt about Topaz.

2 The Smiths' house, with its riot of colours and chaotic untidiness, is in complete contrast to the black and white neatness of Surinder's room of which he is so proud. Describe *your* ideal room. Would it be like either of these, or would it be completely different? How would it reflect your character and the way you would like others to see you?

Peter Lipton's story, 'As Flies to Wanton Boys', tells of a kind of school that has now (thankfully, some would say) largely disappeared. The author's repressive boys' grammar school in the England of the 1950s is very different from the Australian co-educational comprehensive school described by Emily Rodda in her story on p. 99, but, in a curious way, the stories have something in common. Both suggest that pupils can be very cruel to anyone who doesn't 'fit in' and both suggest that experiences like this can have a lasting effect on people in later life.

As Flies to Wanton Boys
Peter Lipton

Denys Vine still troubles my conscience though I swear I wasn't the sole cause of his death. And, after all, it wasn't intentional; we only did it for a laugh.

Denys Vine stands – or stoops, rather – as clear in my memory now as he did in life thirty years ago: shiny blue suit, too short in arm and leg; cracked and battered leather shoes, carefully polished; blue, woollen socks. The collar of his greying shirt had lost all stiffening and was held together at the neck by some sort of college tie, blue again with small gold emblems, the threads of which were beginning to fray, particularly under the fold of pallid skin which continually abraded the worn and shiny knot as he peered to and fro. His pale eyes watering behind thin, metal framed spectacles held together by a yellowing botch of sticky tape, he was a natural victim.

Hesitant, he stood before the class of adolescent boys. The noisy banging of desk lids, the casual slinging of bags and cases to the floor, the unnaturally loud calling to each other across the room were the normal prelude to an RE lesson with 'D. Vine' as he was known.

'Mornin', D. Vine!'

'Wotcher, D. Vine, me old mate.'

'You look Divine, sir!'

The rabble swarmed into the room ready for some fun after a heavy morning of maths and French and history where they had been kept hard at it, subjected in turn to the gruff sarcasm of 'Uncle Sam' Harper, the senile ramblings and unpredictable punishments of old Bill Tate and, worst of all, the vicious contempt of Sharky Surridge who had yet again contrived to beat one of their number during the previous lesson. Sharky loved it; he really did.

Smart, a cool and plausible boy, approached the master's desk and indicated the heavy old reel-to-reel tape-recorder. Not one of these modern cassette jobs but a massive machine weighing forty pounds with twin reels of tape, nearly half a mile of it, wound on detachable aluminium spools. His voice brimmed with politeness.

'I see we are to listen to the tape-recorder, sir. May I be of any assistance, sir?'

'Why, yes, thank you, Smart.'

'Perhaps, sir, if I . . . Ah! I see you have the reels reversed. Lipton, would you be so kind. . ?'

Dexterously the full reel was slipped from the machine, passed behind Divine's back and taken courteously by Lipton who examined it carefully and passed it back in front of the teacher. Unnoticed, a slender loop of tape ran from the machine and encircled the teacher.

'Please. . . all of you . . .sit down at your desks,' Divine called over the rising noise. Gradually the room subsided. Lipton peered uncertainly at the full reel he held in his hand.

'It was side A you wanted, wasn't it, sir?' The two amiable youths were still standing either side of him.

'A? A? Yes, A . . . I think so.'

'Sorry, sir, I've dropped it. Hold on a sec.' The reel unrolled beneath Divine's chair and was retrieved by Smart who passed it once more behind the master to Lipton who clicked it firmly into place on the machine.

'I think that's done it, sir; they're quite tricky, these machines.'

'Yes. Thank you, thank you. I wonder if . . .'

'No problem, sir. Glad to help.'

'Just a tick, sir. I think we've made a mistake, sir. That's the B side you've got on the lefthand reel and you wanted side A, didn't you, sir? – Lipton, pass that reel here.'

Festooned in tape, Divine protested weakly.

'Not to worry, sir, we'll soon have this sorted out for you.'

'I think, perhaps if we got started now . . .' He scanned the room anxiously. Something was different, something had changed. What was it? Why was the fire escape door ajar?

Outside, three floors up on the fire escape, Richards, Bates, Isaacs and Atkinson balanced their desks precariously. The narrow fretted steps of black iron didn't allow much room for manoeuvre, and edging a desk and chair gingerly down to the first landing was tricky, though enjoyable on such a sunny morning.

'Thank you for your help, Lipton, Smart. I really think I can manage now.' Solicitously they sat him down in his chair, deftly looping the tape twice more around him as they did so.

Outside, the queue of desks down the fire escape lengthened to the second landing and the room was noticeably empty.

It needed skill to transport a desk and chair across the ever-growing space without attracting Divine's attention. Smart and Lipton redoubled their efforts, smoothing down Divine's jacket, brushing imaginary chalk dust off his lapels, talking good-naturedly all the time in reassuring tones as though to one younger than themselves. Divine, completely unaware of what was happening, turned from one to the other, mesmerised by their talk as the spool was passed adroitly from hand to hand and the room steadily emptied.

'Of course, sir, this is the old ferric tape, isn't it, sir? Do you know about the new metal tape, sir? The new machines that are coming in are much smaller than this, aren't they, sir? My father's thinking of getting one. I wonder which type of machine you would advise, sir?'

At last it was done. Outside, twenty-eight pupils had balanced twenty-eight desks and chairs in a zig-zag the height of the building, edged their way past them and disappeared into the gloom of the cloakrooms below.

'I think you'll find that's fixed it, sir. May we be excused, sir?' Without awaiting a reply, they were gone.

At break Mr Wilson entered the empty classroom. Sunlight streamed through the windows, projecting the patterns of tall frames at an angle across the rough floorboarding. Scraps of paper, pencil stubs, tacks, an apple core, a couple of empty desks, but nothing else, met his gaze.

'What the . . .?' Three brisk strides took him to where a hunched figure swathed in what appeared to be thin ribbon, huddled, rocking slightly to and fro.

'Smart and Lipton said you were a bit tied up when I met them in the corridor just now, but this . . .' The figure didn't respond.

Mr Wilson cut him free and sent him home. He never returned. Six weeks later we heard he'd died.

No details were forthcoming but . . . we knew. The open verdict rated just two paragraphs in the local rag.

A teacher myself now for twenty or more years, barely a week goes by when I don't think of old Divine, and boys who approach me with a courteous 'Do you need any help, Mr Lipton?' are often surprised to find themselves rudely rebuffed.

Inside the story

In pairs or small groups

1 We are not told about anything Mr Vine had done to deserve the treatment he received, so why do you think the boys behaved as they did towards him? You might like to think about hints we are given as to the kind of school being described and how boys in such an atmosphere would regard a teacher like Mr Vine.

2 What sort of characters are Lipton and Smith? What does the manner in which they speak and behave suggest about them?

3 The boys probably thought that what they did was amusing. Is it a funny story?

4 How do you think the writer feels about the incident he is describing? Do you think it is based on something that really happened, or is it 'just a story'?

5 How do *you* feel about D. Vine? How do you feel about Mr Lipton? Do you have any sympathy for either?

On your own

We learn that Lipton has been a teacher for over twenty years since the time of the story. He lets us know only two things about himself as an adult. Imagine what sort of teacher he is likely to have turned into and write a description of him. You may find it helpful to look again at the description of Mr Vine in the second and third paragraphs of the story and to describe how you see Mr Lipton as he stands before a class. How might he be different? Imagine what he is like physically, how he stands, walks, dresses; imagine how he speaks and how he behaves to his pupils. What does he think about when they misbehave?

THE AUTHORS

James Berry was born and grew up in Jamaica and now lives both there and in Sussex. He is a distinguished writer and poet who in 1982 won the National Poetry Society's Annual Prize. His first book for children, *A Thief in the Village*, won the Smarties Prize in 1987.

Ray Bradbury was born in 1920 in Illinois, USA. His first published work appeared in sci-fi magazines, but he rapidly established himself as a leading novelist and short story writer who brings the future unnervingly into the present. *The Illustrated Man* and *The Golden Apples of The Sun* are two of his best known short story collections.

Timothy Callender was born in Barbados and educated at the University of the West Indies and at London University. A writer, painter and teacher, both in secondary schools and on the UWI campus, his stories have been published as a collection, *It So Happen*.

Angela Carter was born in 1940, read English at Bristol University and spent two years living in Japan. From 1976 to 1978, she was Fellow in Creative Writing at Sheffield University and in 1980–81 she was visiting Professor on the Writing Programme at Brown University, Providence, Rhode Island. Her first novel was published in 1965. She wrote several novels, three collections of short stories and translated the Fairy Stories of Charles Perrault. More recently, she edited *The Virago Book of Fairy Stories* from which the tale in this book is taken. She died in 1992.

Leon Garfield was born in 1921 and is well known as a writer of children's historical novels and some short stories. Author of *Devil in the Fog*, *Jack Holborn*, *Smith* and numerous others, he has won the Guardian Children's Fiction prize and the Carnegie Medal.

Susan Gregory was born in 1945 in Redhill, England. She studied at the University of

Nottingham, and has written extensively for children.

Eamon Kelly has been described as 'Ireland's supreme storyteller'. He draws upon a vast knowledge of folk-tales and legends for his stories which are, first and foremost, for *telling*, though 'The House Under the Sea' is one of several he has written down in his collection, *The Bridge of Feathers* (1989).

Rudyard Kipling (1865–1936) was born in Bombay and as a small child was brought up by an Indian nurse, becoming bilingual in English and Hindustani. He was sent to England to be educated at the United Services College. He returned to India in 1882 and worked as a journalist, publishing stories and poems in various journals. These were later published in book form. He returned to live in England in 1889 and published his *Just So Stories* (1902), *The Jungle Book* and *Puck of Pook's Hill* which established him as a major children's writer. *Kim* was published in 1901.

Peter Lipton was born in 1942 and attended a boys' grammar school in Yorkshire. His stories are often based on his experiences there, which continue, he claims, to haunt him.

Lucian was a Greek writer born around AD 120 at Samosata on the banks of the Euphrates. He wrote satirical *Dialogues* about the failings of the society of his time and in his *Veracious History* – from which the extract in this book is taken – he provided the prototype for *Gulliver's Travels*.

Ruth Manning-Sanders was born in Swansea, Wales

in 1888. A well-loved author and editor, she is best-known for her re-tellings of regional tales and fairy stories. She died in 1988 (her centenary year) in Penzance, Cornwall.

Jan Mark was born in 1943 in Welwyn, Herts and brought up in Ashford, Kent. She attended Canterbury College of Art and then taught for six years in a secondary school in Gravesend. She is now a freelance writer known mainly for her children's fiction. She has won the Carnegie Medal, The Observer Teenage Fiction Award, the Penguin/Guardian Award, and the Angel Literary Prize. From 1982 to 1984, she held an Arts Council Fellowship in Writing at Oxford Polytechnic. Her works include *Thunder and Lightnings*, *Hairs in the Palm of your Hand* and many more.

Sybil Marshall was born and brought up in the fen country where she lives now in her retirement at Ely. She spent her life in the field of education, first as a gifted teacher and later as a university lecturer.

Edna O'Brien was born in 1930 in Co. Clare, Ireland and now lives in London. She has written five collections of short stories and ten novels including *Country Girls*, as well as scripts and film screenplays. She won the Yorkshire Post Novel award in 1971.

Sean O'Faolain was born in Dublin in 1900 and educated at the National University of Ireland and at Harvard. In 1929 he became lecturer in English at Boston College and then at Strawberry Hill College. His first book was published in 1932.

Susan Price has written historical and contemporary novels, ghost stories and fantasies. She won the Carnegie Medal in 1988 for *The Ghost Drum*.

Rudolph Erich Raspe (1737–94) was born in Hanover. While working as librarian at Cassel, he stole jewels from the Landgraf's collection and fled to England. He supplemented his income by publishing his version of Baron Munchausen's adventures.

Emily Rodda is Australian and has twice won Children's Book Council Awards – in 1985 for *Something Special* and in 1987 for *Pigs Might Fly*.

Sean Thomas was four years old when the 'story' he told was written down by his father.